CW00430488

OPTAVIA DIET COOKBOOK

The Easy and Complete Guide to Losing Weight With Quick and Affordable Recipes That Even Beginners on a Budget and Busy People Can do. Start Your Long-Lasting Transformation

Susan Hull

© **Copyright 2021 by Susan Hull - All rights reserved.**

This document is geared towards providing exact and reliable information in regard to the topic and issue covered.

- From a Declaration of Principles which was accepted and approved equally by a Committee of the American Bar Association and a Committee of Publishers and Associations.

In no way is it legal to reproduce, duplicate, or transmit any part of this document in either electronic means or in printed format. All rights reserved.

The information provided herein is stated to be truthful and consistent, in that any liability, in terms of inattention or otherwise, by any usage or abuse of any policies, processes, or directions contained within is the solitary and utter responsibility of the recipient reader. Under no circumstances will any legal responsibility or blame be held against the publisher for any reparation, damages, or monetary loss due to the information herein, either directly or indirectly.

Respective authors own all copyrights not held by the publisher.

The information herein is offered for informational purposes solely and is universal as so. The presentation of the information is without contract or any type of guarantee assurance.

The trademarks that are used are without any consent, and the publication of the trademark is without permission or backing by the trademark owner. All trademarks and brands within this book are for clarifying purposes only

Table of Content

Introduction 8

    What Is Optavia? 9

    Various Optavia Diet Plans 10

    How to Start This Diet 11

    How to Manage This Diet 11

    How to Maintain the Desired Results 11

Chapter 1.   Why Optavia Is So Special? 12

    What Is the Perfect Target of People? 12

    Optavia Diet Plans FAQs 13

Chapter 2.   What Do You Eat On Optavia? 15

    How Often Do You Eat on Optavia? 17

Chapter 3.   How Does Optavia Diet Work For Weight Loss? 19

Chapter 4.   Foods I Can Eat On the Optavia Diet 22

    What Can I Eat? 22

    What Can I Not Eat? 23

Chapter 5.   What Advantages Does The Optavia Diet Offer? 25

Chapter 6.   What Are The Drawbacks Of An Optavia Diet? 27

    1. High Monthly Cost 27

    2. Includes Processed Foods 27

    3. Fast Recovery of Lost Weight 27

    4. Excessive Calorie Restriction 27

    5. Boredom and Isolation During Meals 28

Chapter 7.   Meal Planner + Shopping List 29

Chapter 8.   Fueling Recipes 34

    1.   Smooth Peanut Butter Cream 34

2. Peanut Butter Crunch Bars 35

3. Chocolate Crunch Cookies 37

4. Brownie Ice Cream Sandwiches 40

5. Grilled Cheese Tomato Sandwich 43

6. Slutty Brownie 45

7. Chocolate Chip Cakes 48

8. Pudding Pies 51

9. Chocolate Coconut Cake 53

10. Sweet Potato Protein Pancakes 56

11. Mexican Meatloaf 58

Chapter 9.   Chicken Recipes 60

12. Tender Taco Chicken 60

13. Basil Chicken Sausage & Zucchini Spaghetti 62

14. Orange Chicken 64

15. Spinach and Mushroom Stuffed Chicken 66

16. Rosemary Chicken 68

17. Stuffed Chicken Breasts with Tomato Salad 70

18. Feta Chicken with Zucchini 71

19. Cinnamon Chicken 73

20. Chinese Five Spice Chicken 75

21. Chicken with Acorn Squash and Tomatoes 77

22. Chicken Cordon Bleu 79

Chapter 10.   Pork Recipes 81

23. Brown Sugar Italian Pork 81

24. Apricot-Glazed Pork Chops 82

25. Easy Pork Ribs 83

26. Pineapple-BBQ Pork 84

27.   Apple-Garlic Pork Loin 85

28.   Garden Herb New York Strip Steaks 86

29.   Orange Pork and Broccoli Stir-Fry 88

Chapter 11.   Soup Recipes 90

30.   Chicken Enchilada Soup 90

31.   Buffalo Chicken Soup 92

32.   Slow Cooker Taco Soup 94

33.   Wedding Soup 95

34.   Teriyaki Sauce 97

35.   Turmeric & Lemon Dressing 98

36.   Garlic Vinaigrette 99

37.   Thai Salsa 100

38.   Walnut Vinaigrette 102

39.   Walnut & Mint Pesto 103

40.   Black Bean soup 104

41.   Cold Tomato Summer Vegetable Soup 106

Chapter 12.   Dessert Recipes 108

42.   Yogurt Mint 108

43.   Chocolate Fondue 109

44.   Rice Pudding 110

45.   Braised Apples 111

46.   Wine Figs 112

47.   Mint Chocolate Cheesecake Cupcakes 113

Chapter 13.   Breakfast Recipes 115

48.   Optavia Biscuit Pizza 115

49.   Lean and Green Smoothie 1 117

50.   Lean and Green Smoothie 2 119

51.   Cinnamon Crescent Rolls 120

52.   Mushroom Scrambled Eggs 122

53.   Turkey Breakfast Sausages 124

54.   Blueberry Pancakes 125

55.   Banana Pecan Muffins 127

56.   Banana and Blueberry Muffins 129

57.   Sweet Potato Hash 131

58.   Crunchy and Chewy Granola 133

Chapter 14.   Lunch Recipes 135

59.   Beef Burgers 135

60.   Salmon Burgers 137

61.   Meatballs with Salad 139

62.   Stuffed Bell Peppers 141

63.   Shrimp with Spinach 143

64.   Scallops with Broccoli 145

65.   Kale and Red Onion Dhal with Buckwheat 147

66.   Lamb, Butternut Squash and Date Tagine 149

67.   Baked Potatoes with Spicy Chickpea Stew 152

68.   Char-Grilled Steak 154

69.   Asian King Prawn Stir-Fry Together with Buckwheat Noodles 156

70.   Fruity Curry Chicken Salad 158

Chapter 15.   Dinner Recipes 160

71.   Garlicky Tomato Chicken Casserole 160

72.   Chicken Cacciatore 162

73.   Cauliflower Curry 164

74.   Herbed Roasted Chicken Breasts 166

75.   Seafood Paella 168

76. Full-of-veg hash recipe 170

77. Sweet Potato Curry Recipe 172

78. Carrot, Courgette and Halloumi Hamburgers 174

79. Minted Lamb with a Couscous Salad Recipe 176

80. Pesto Salmon Pasta Noodles 178

81. Chicken liver along with tomato ragu 180

82. Rita's 'rowdy' enchiladas 182

Chapter 16. Lean and Green 184

83. Sizzling Chicken Fajita Salad 184

84. Triumph of Cucumbers and Avocados 186

85. Crab and Asparagus Frittata 188

86. Broccoli Cheese Breakfast Casserole 190

87. Bibimbap Bowls 192

88. Mini Bacon Cheeseburger Bites 195

89. Mongolian Beef 197

90. Taco Mason Jar Salad 199

91. Easy Salmon Florentine 201

92. Shrimp and Creamy Cauliflower Grits 203

Conclusion 205

Introduction

With the Optavia diet, you can reach your body shape and size of your choice. Every Optavia weight-loss plan offers an extensive list of healthy, delicious, and easy to make. One can also pick from among the numerous weight-loss meal options.

A healthier life is not something anyone can afford to delay today. This is the time to make those positive changes that can benefit you always. Optavia diet was created with just the right formula and care to offer the healthiest weight-loss solutions. Many people have found Optavia to be the only diet to offer a sensible weight-loss program and a healthy diet menu. Let's understand what the healthy diet menu is.

How can I use the weight-loss diet plans?

Optavia approaches to weight loss are quite different from other diet plans as they are realistic and make you know you are not suffering from a temporary problem. Here the weight loss is gradual and continuous for a healthy life.

You will be able to bring about a safe and gradual change in your body that works to meet your every goal.

The Optavia diet is carefully designed in a way that will help you lose weight safely and naturally. Getting rid of unwanted pounds is the main objective of this diet plan. You will always get the perfect weight you wish.

In this diet, you can find a comprehensive list of proper portions. Most of the recipes are low in fat and protein and high in fiber. The general diet plan is appropriate for most adults and contains no harmful chemicals, drugs, or steroids.

Tips for Weight Reduction

The Optavia plan has cooking and exercise options that you can follow. This plan will help you lose up to 20 pounds in a month. You can also use the weight-loss diet plan for a long time or a quick weight-loss plan. You can also use these plans to improve your overall health.

Why can the Optavia diet make a good weight-loss program?

Most of the diet plans only offer weight loss in a short period. If you opt for a weight-loss plan that offers long-term results, you will find the weight-loss result will take time to achieve. This type of program will help you apply yourself to change your eating habits.

The weight loss comes with the side of a healthy mood and increased energy levels. It will also help you maintain your weight if you move to the maintenance phase.

How can you use an Optavia diet plan that offers a healthy diet menu?

One of the best parts of Optavia is that it helps you choose from among the weight loss meal options. Just go to the Optavia website and sign up for a personal account. Once you receive your personalized Optavia meal plan, follow it religiously. Your Optavia strategy will work perfectly for you if you start working correctly from day one.

You can ask the company consultants for specific guidelines on how to make the right meal choices. These recipes are not as good as we would like them to be, but you can use them for now. Once you are eating right, you will never look for a different diet plan like this one.

The items in the Optavia healthy diet menu are made using the right proportion of fat, carbohydrates, protein and fiber. This is just the sort of diet you want to stick to for the rest of your life.

All the biggest diet and get-skinny programs in the world follow this type of diet, which's a fact. You will struggle with these diets if you do not eat the right type of foods. Eating the right food is the secret to losing weight.

This diet plan offers optimal weight change and a healthy diet menu. This makes it the safest weight-loss plan in the world. There is no need to take any kind of supplements or drugs. Just follow the Optavia diet plan and you are on the right path to a healthy life.

What Is Optavia?

When hearing of Medifast, you are acquainted with the plan, as Optavia is an important version of Medifast. As planned by Medifast, the Optavia diet is pre-packed with low-calorie mini-dishes called "Fuelings" – and ready-to-eat snacks right at your door.

Over 60 different portions of "fuel" options, including shawls, bars, shelves (pasta and cheese) – even brownies. According to the company, each fuel is protein-based and contains probiotics for the digestive system.

The Optavia Diet encourages people to limit the number of calories that they should take daily. To make this possible, dieters are motivated to choose healthier food items and meal replacements. But unlike other types of commercial diet regimens, the Optavia Diet comes in different variations that one can choose according to the needs.

Various Optavia Diet Plans

- **5&1 Optavia diet plan**: This is the most common version of the Optavia Diet. This one includes consuming five pre-packed meals from them and one home-made balanced dinner.
- **4&2&1 Optavia diet plan**: This diet plan is designed for people who want to have flexibility while following this regimen. Under this program, dieters are encouraged to eat more calories and have more flexible food choices. It means that they can finish four pre-packed Optimal Health Fuelings food, three home-cooked meals from the Lean and Green, and one snack daily.
- **5&2&2 Optavia diet plan**: This diet plan is perfect for individuals who prefer to have a flexible one to achieve a healthy weight. It is recommended for a wide variety of people. Under this diet regimen, dieters must eat five fueling, two lean and green meals, and two healthy snacks.
- **3&3 Optavia diet plan**: This diet plan is created for people who have moderate weight problems and merely want to maintain a healthy body. Under this diet plan, dieters are encouraged to consume three prepackaged Optimal Health Fuelings and three home-cooked meals.
- **Optavia for nursing mothers**: This diet regimen is designed for nursing mothers with babies of at least two months old. Aside from supporting breastfeeding mothers, it also encourages gradual weight-loss.
- **Optavia for diabetes**: This Optavia Diet plan is designed for diabetes type 1 and 2. The meal plans are developed to consume more green and lean meals, depending on their needs and condition.
- **Optavia for gout**: This diet regimen incorporates a balance of low in purines and moderate in protein.
- **Optavia for seniors (65 years and older)**: this is designed for seniors. The Optavia Diet plan has some variations following the components of fuelings, depending on the senior dieters' needs and activities.
- **Optavia for teen boys and teen girls (13–18 years old)**: Designed for active teens, the Optavia for Teens Boys and Optavia for Teens Girls provide the right nutrition to growing teens.

Regardless of which type of Optavia Diet plan you choose; you must talk with someone to coach you. He will assist you in determining which method is right for you based on your individual goals. It is to ensure that you get the most out of the program you have chosen.

How to Start This Diet

The Optavia Diet is comprised of different phases. A certified coach will educate you on the steps you need to undertake to follow this regimen. Considering those people who are new to this diet, below are some of the matters that you need to know when starting with this diet regimen.

How to Manage This Diet

During this phase, people are encouraged to consume 800 to 1,000 calories to help them shed off at least 12 pounds within the next 12 weeks. For instance, if you are following the 5&1 Optavia Diet Plan, you need to eat one meal every 2 or 3 hours and include a 30-minute moderate workout on most days of your week. You need to consume not more than 100g rams of carbs daily during this phase.

This phase also encourages the dieter to include one optional snack per day, such as ½ cup of sugar-free gelatin, three celery sticks and 12 ounces of nuts. Aside from these things, below are other things that you need to remember when following this phase:

- Ensure that the portion size recommendations are for cooked weight and not the raw one of your ingredients.
- Opt for meals that are baked, grilled, broiled or poached. Avoid frying foods, as this will increase your calorie intake.
- You need to consume fish that are rich in Omega-3 fatty acids, at least two servings. These include fishes like tuna, salmon, trout, mackerel, herring and other cold-water fishes.
- Choose meatless alternatives like tofu and tempeh.
- Follow the program even when you are dining out. Keep in mind that drinking alcohol is discouraged when following this plan.

How to Maintain the Desired Results

When you reach your weight goals, the next phase is the transition stage. It is a 6-week stage that involves increasing your calorie intake to 1,550 per day. You can also add more varieties into your meal, such as whole grains, low-fat dairy, and fruits.

After six weeks, you can now move into the 3&3 Optavia Diet plan, so you must eat three Lean and Green meals and 3 Fueling foods.

Chapter 1. **Why Optavia Is So Special?**

Linked to the Medifast plan, the Optavia Diet focuses primarily on mixes, snacks, and processed meals, with at least one low-carbohydrate meal — known as "Lean Green Meal"—that you cook on your own.

How Optavia differs from the initial Medifast plan is that you don't have to attend a doctor's clinic to sign up for or order items for the Optavia Diet. Getting started basically involves literally registering and paying electronically to get your first package delivered to you. And this facility, together with direct marketing and social networking, has undoubtedly played a significant role in making Optavia a common brand in the field of weight loss.

Thanks to the dynamic approach of Optavia, US World Report rated # 2 on their Best Quick Weight-Loss Diets ranking. Apart from being at the top of the Best Diets chart, some amazing help and ease are given to customers to make their weight-loss journey smoother:

1.   It is easy to pick a plan and order, and automated fulfillment is possible. The most complicated directions for OPTAVIA meals include the inclusion of water and microwaving. Food preparation is easy. It should be possible for even untrained cooks to easily tackle the lean and green dinner.

2.   OPTAVIA mentors seek to help you develop healthier practices, allowing you access to weekly and monthly calls to give support, group activities, and the wellness support network, which comprises experts such as licensed dietitians while becoming part of the OPTAVIA network. A variety of detailed guides and FAQs can also be downloaded online for free.

3.   Medifast also notes that its meals have a strong "fullness index," which indicates that the high quality of protein and fiber can leave you feeling satiated for longer. Experts on nutrition discuss the value of satiety, the relaxed sensation that you have had plenty.

What Is the Perfect Target of People?

The simplicity of meal replacement programs that take the guessing out of weight management has long attracted customers. That's why the successful meal-replacement program in Optavia Diet is suggested for individuals who are too busy to prepare all three meals daily. It also reduces the hassle of shopping for each and every item by offering a range of food options in fueling and supplying them to doorsteps.

The Optavia Diet is essentially intended to shed more than 15lbs of weight for healthier adults. However, they still provide programs that can be customized to fit with those with specific fitness or lifestyle conditions. Optavia provides suggestions for adults over 65 and inactive, individuals who are quite active, people who have little weight to lose, persons who choose to add more carbs into their diet, pregnant moms, and plans for people with gout. It specifies that it should be practiced with a specialist's guidance for those with diabetes type 1 or type 2. Also, for those aged 13 and 18 years, it provides a teenage package, making it one of the relatively few consumer diets accessible for teenagers.

Optavia Diet Plans FAQs

You may have some questions about the Optavia Diet Plan. Below are some of the common FAQs that people ask about this diet regimen:

Which program is right for me?

Optavia offers a wide variety of programs that are designed to improve health and well-being. Choosing the right one is easy as these diet plans are designed for different individuals and their needs. However, if you are still not sure about which diet plan to follow, you can always get in touch with an Optavia coach to learn about the many options that you have.

Is it okay for me to skip fuelings?

Fuelings is very important as it is specifically formulated with the right balance of macronutrients (carbohydrates, fats and protein). Proper fueling can help promote an efficient fat-burning state so that people lose fat without losing their energy. If you skip fueling, you might miss out on these important nutrients, including your daily dose of vitamins and minerals. Now, if you accidentally skip your fuelings within 24 hours, it is crucial to double up so that you don't miss the nutrition provided by your fuelings.

Which plan is best for my level of fitness?

Exercise can lead to lifelong transformation. This is the reason why a specific Optavia Diet plan is designed for people who have different activity levels. Active adults who engage in 45 minutes of light to moderate exercise can benefit from the 5&1 Plan. Always talk to your coach about which plan is great for your age and activity level.

Can I rearrange my fuelings especially if I work on long days or night duty?

Yes. You can rearrange the timing of your fuelings depending on your schedule. What is important is that you consume your fuelings and lean and green meals within 24 hours. So, whether you work at night or on regular hours, make sure that you eat your meals every 2 or 3 hours throughout the time that you are awake.

How often should I eat my meals?

The Optavia Diet plan teaches you the habit of eating healthy. You are encouraged to eat six small meals daily. As mentioned earlier, you are encouraged to eat every two to three hours from your waking time. Thus, start your day with fuelings and eat your lean and green meals in between your fuelings. It is recommended that you eat your first meal within an hour of waking to ensure optimal blood sugar. This is also a good strategy for hunger control.

Chapter 2. **What Do You Eat On Optavia?**

Fuelings

The Optavia Diet is famous for its Optavia fuelings that involve pre-packaged foods that dieters can eat. There are more than 60 soups, shakes, bars, and other fueling products that you can consume as your meal replacements.

Although Fuelings can mainly supply the bulk of your daily calories (ranging from 800 to 1,000), you can still create your own "Good & Green" meals consisting of lean protein, non-starchy vegetables and healthy fats.

Optavia Fuelings are Optavia Food items. Classic Fuelings, Critical Fuelings and Select Fuelings are eligible. During your weight-reduction path, you will pick from more than 60 fuelings to use as supplements. Optavia Critical Fuelings provides Decadent Double Chocolate Brownie, Crispy Buttermilk Cheddar Pie, Smooth Raspberry or Wild Strawberry Drink and much more. Optavia Fuelings contains 24 vitamins and nutrients, useful content, full protein, probiotic proprietary GanedenBC30 and no artificial colors, flavors, or sweeteners.

Optavia Pick Fuelings include internationally influenced recipes. They are often produced with non-GMO foods from across the globe. You will pick from 13 Fuelings featuring robust flavors and foreign ingredients such as Bolivian chia seeds, Mediterranean rosemary and Indonesian cinnamon. The number of fuelings you'll have per day will depend on the weight-reduction plan you're on.

Lean Meat

Lean and green meals require you to make foods out of lean meats. There are three categories of lean meats identified by Optavia, including (1) lean, (2) leaner and (3) leanest. Lean meats include salmon, pork chops and lamb while leaner meats include chicken breasts and swordfish. The leanest meats include egg whites, shrimp and cod.

Greens and Non-starchy Vegetables

Optavia's 5&1 plan permits for two non-starchy vegetables together with the protein in your lean and green meal.

The vegetables are allocated into lower, moderate, and higher carbohydrate categories, such as:

- **Lower carb**: salad greens.
- **Moderate carb**: cauliflower or summer squash.
- **Higher Carb**: broccoli or peppers.

This will discuss the green servings that you still need to consume while following the Optavia Diet Plan. These include all kinds of vegetables that have been categorized from lower, moderate, and high in terms of carbohydrate content. One serving of vegetables should be at ½ cup unless otherwise specified.

Lower Carbohydrates. These are vegetables that contain low amounts of carbohydrates. If you are following the 5&1 Optavia Diet plan, then these vegetables are good for you:

- A cup of green leafy vegetables, such as collard greens (raw), lettuce (green leaf, iceberg, butterhead and romaine), spinach (raw), mustard greens, spring mix, bok choy (raw), and watercress.
- ½ cup of vegetables including cucumbers, celery, radishes, white mushroom, sprouts (mung bean, alfalfa), arugula, turnip greens, escarole, nopales, Swiss chard (raw), jalapeno, and bok choy (cooked).

Moderate Carbohydrates. These are vegetables that contain moderate amounts of carbohydrates. Below are the types of vegetables that can be consumed in moderation:

- ½ cup of any of the following vegetables, such as asparagus, cauliflower, a fennel bulb, eggplant, portabella mushrooms, kale, cooked spinach, summer squash (zucchini and scallop).

Higher Carbohydrates. Foods that are under this category contain a high amount of starch. Make sure to consume limited amounts of these vegetables:

- ½ cup of the following vegetables like chayote squash, red cabbage, broccoli, cooked collard and mustard greens, green or wax beans, kohlrabi, kabocha squash, cooked leeks, any peppers, okra, raw scallion, summer squash such as straight neck and crookneck, tomatoes, spaghetti squash, turnips, jicama, cooked Swiss chard and hearts of palm.

Healthy Fats

Healthy fats are encouraged for people who follow the Optavia Diet. These include healthy fats such as olive oil, walnut oil, flaxseed and avocado. However, it is important to consume two servings of healthy fats to still keep up with the Optavia Diet.

Low-Fat Dairy, Fresh Fruit, and Whole Grains

Once dieters are able to achieve their weight-loss goals through meal replacements, they can start consuming other foods to maintain their ideal weight. These include low-fat dairy, fresh fruits and whole grains. You can also consume meatless alternatives including 2 cups egg substitute, and 5 ounces seitan. For low-fat dairy, you are allowed to consume 1 ½ cups 1% cottage cheese and 12 ounces of non-fat Greek yogurt.

How Often Do You Eat on Optavia?

Optavia indicates that you should eat six or seven times a day (approximately a few hours each) depending on the arrangement. The three available plans are:

- The optimal weight 5&1 Plan,

- Optimal weight 4&2&1 Plan, and

- Optimal health 3&3 Program

Basically, each plan consists of a certain number of "Fuelings". These fuelings are prepackaged meals and snacks that make up a major portion of the Optavia diet. They're provided by the Optavia brand.

The 5&1 Plan: The 5&1 plan involves eating five "Fuelings" every day in addition to one homemade low-calorie "lean and green" meal. This is the most common plan for people trying to lose weight fast. So basically, you stick to just one meal per day along with the prescribed fuelings. Typically, followers of this program lose between 10-12 pounds after 12 weeks of consistently observing the recommendations.

The 4&2&1 Plan: This plan introduces a little more flexibility to your meals. You get to eat four fuelings in a day, two homemade "lean and green meals" of your own, and one healthy snack from the Optavia brand. This can also be a snack of your choosing such as fruits, dairy products, etc. Our recipes include many more options you can use in this case. Even with the flexibility of this plan, you can still achieve your weight-loss goal.

The Optimal Health 3&3 Plan: This option involves more home cooking than the previous two. The idea here is weight maintenance. It is designed for folks who want to maintain their weight rather than losing weight. It consists of eating three "fuelings" per day and cooking three low-calorie "lean and green" meals to go with it.

The Optavia diet recipes are quite easy to make and are nutritious as well. We've provided easy-to-apply guidelines for each listed recipe. You may also join the online community facilitated by the company to learn from others and get encouragement as you follow the recipes. Enrollees are also able to access the robust coaching program provided by the company, thereby leveraging a good avenue for getting answers to questions. As soon as you've achieved your goal weight, it's easy to begin your transition off the program. Typically, the optimal health 3&3 plan provides a soft landing for you. And since your old eating habits have been replaced by a new and healthier one, you won't have to struggle with maintaining a healthy lifestyle. As mentioned earlier, exercise is key and highly encouraged even as you go with the recipes. However, according to expert recommendations, if you're already very active in exercises, you may want to soft-pedal and reduce the intensity of, but not stop physical activities while on the program.

Chapter 3. **How Does Optavia Diet Work For Weight Loss?**

The OPTAVIA 5 & 1 weight-loss plan is designed to help you lose 12 lbs in 12 weeks. Calories are restricted to only 800 to 1000 per day (McGrane, 2020).

A lower calorie intake is certainly what is needed for losing unwanted weight, while still consuming enough balanced nutrients to function optimally during an average day. The ideal condition to aim for is caloric balance —that is when the calories consumed are roughly the calories burned in a day (Szalay, 2015).

The OPTAVIA diet promises to deliver on both lower calories as well as balanced nutrition (OPTAVIA, n.d.).

Calories Matter

While counting calories have become modern buzzwords, the term also is frequently misunderstood in terms of nutrition vs weight loss.

Definition of Calorie

A calorie is a measurement of energy. In terms of nutrition, it can be described as the amount of food that is needed to provide enough energy for one large calorie (Merriam-Webster, 2019).

A calorie was originally defined in science as the amount of heat needed to raise the temperature of one kilogram of water one degree Celsius from zero. In 1925, physicists coined the term 'joule', which referred to the energy needed to move a one-newton unit for a distance of one meter. One calorie is equal to 4.18 joules (Szalay, 2015).

Different nutrients contain standard amounts of calories. One ounce of boneless cooked chicken for instance contains 67 calories, while one ounce of baked potato only contains 26 calories (Calories and nutrition, 2019).

High, Low and Empty Calories Explained

The number of calories present in an item of food determines whether the food is classified as low or high calorie.

When talking about high-calorie diets, it is usually junk food or sweets that spring to mind. Some healthy foods, however, also pack a mighty calorie punch. Oils, avocado, quinoa and dried fruits are examples of foods that are very dense in calorie content. One serving of one of these contains far more calories than a serving of equivalent size of low-calorie food. One-quarter cup of raisins will deliver the same number of calories as one cup of fresh grapes, for instance (Szalay, 2015).

In contrast, vegetables and fresh fruits are seen as low-calorie foods. The number of calories is low in comparison to the size of the serving. To illustrate, one cup of broccoli florets contains only 20 calories, whereas one cup of quinoa delivers a whopping 636 calories (Szalay, 2015).

Empty calories are found in items that contain virtually no or very few nutrients. Enjoying ice cream on a hot day may be very refreshing, but your body will not be nourished by the calories in the ice cream. Foods that get sugars or solid fats added in the manufacturing and preparation processes fall in this category (Szalay, 2015).

The Role of Calories in Weight Loss

Food supplies energy to the body. It provides the fuel a human body needs to function optimally and should ideally be used up before the next meal.

It, therefore, stands to reason that any surplus food which has been converted to energy but not used during active hours has to go somewhere. It needs to be stored and that is where fat cells come in.

The small bulbous spheres called adipocytes got a bad reputation when being skinny came into fashion some decades ago, but they are indispensable for our wellbeing. In addition to storing fat, they play an important role in regulating temperature among other things (Pappas, 2018).

They are also important in the removal of excess blood sugar from the blood and perform a vital function in the immune system (Pappas, 2018).

If the number of calories that come into the body is reduced such as is the case on the OPTAVIA diet, the body is forced to use its stores in the adipocytes for energy and excess fat disappears.

Staying Balanced

The flip side of the calorie coin is to maintain a balanced intake of all the necessary nutrients when cutting back on calories. Simply eating less in a day does not automatically equal health and energy.

An imbalanced intake of nutrients can make us more vulnerable to diseases and infections and can cause lethargy and impaired cognitive function (Krans, 2020). It will also influence the metabolic rate negatively, which will slow down the fat-burning process (Szalay, 2015).

OPTAVIA's Fuelings are designed to provide enough balanced calories to lose weight on the 5 & 1 and 4 & 2 & 1 plans, and to maintain your ideal weight on the Optimal Health plan (OPTAVIA, n.d.). Their products are fortified with minerals and vitamins to meet the nutrient requirements of different ages and certain health conditions. They also describe their products as 'clean', meaning free of artificial colorings and sweeteners (OPTAVIA, n.d.).

Exercise and Weight Loss on OPTAVIA

It's an accepted fact that exercising and working out burn calories. If you use more energy than what is needed for general daily activities, extra energy is required and used. In a diet where the calorie intake is restricted, exercise will (in theory) help burn fat even faster.

With that said, there is a note of caution on exercising from OPTAVIA. According to their website, an exercise program should not be started at the same time as the diet. The body already has much to cope with when a low-calorie meal program is started and the company recommends waiting two or three weeks after completing the program before starting workouts.

If you are on the 5 & 1 plan and have been exercising regularly up to that point, OPTAVIA recommends cutting the duration and intensity in half for the first few weeks (OPTAVIA, n.d.).

Chapter 4. **Foods I Can Eat On the Optavia Diet**

What Can I Eat?

Depending on the plan you choose, you will consume 2 to 5 packed meals (Fuelings) per day. You will prepare and eat 1–3 of your low-calorie meals, mainly non-starchy vegetables and lean protein.

Healthy Fats

Aside from the non-starchy vegetables and lean protein, you can prepare a Lean and Green meal, which can be about two servings of healthy fats such as avocado, flaxseed, walnut, or olive oil.

Greens and Non-Starchy Vegetables

The Optimal Weight 5&1 plan gives two non-starchy vegetables with the protein you will get in your Lean and Green meal.

The vegetables are divided into higher, moderate, and lower carbohydrate categories such as:

- **Higher Carb**: Peppers or Broccoli

- **Moderate Carb**: Summer squash or Cauliflower

- **Lower Carb**: Salad greens

Lean Meats

You need to make provision for 5-7 ounces of cooked lean protein in your Lean and Green meals. Below is the classification of the protein sources, according to Optavia:

- **Lean**: Pork chops, lamb, or salmon

- **Leaner**: Chicken breast or swordfish

- **Leanest**: Egg whites, shrimp, and cod

Optavia Fuelings

The majority of what you will consume while on the Optavia diet will be its pre-packed "fuelings," and you have about 60 options to choose from; it comprises pretzels, shakes, bars, soups, brownies, and other products. Each of the "fuelings" is touted to have an almost identical nutrition profile, so they can be eaten interchangeably.

Whole Grains, Fresh Fruit and Low-Fat Dairy

Once you achieve your desired body weight through non-starchy vegetables, lean protein and meal replacements, the next thing is to move to a plan focusing on maintaining your weight. While on the weight maintenance plan such as the Optimal Health 3&3 Plan, you will get the option of consuming whole grains, fresh fruit and low-fat dairy.

What Can I Not Eat?

Even though the company does not formally prohibit any foods, it advises against consuming less healthy foods that won't give you valuable nutrition or support to your weight-loss goals.

Alcohol

You are expected to limit your alcohol consumption or stay away from it, especially on the Optimal Weight 5&1 Plan.

Sugary Beverages

Consumption of sweetened beverages is strongly discouraged since they can add calories without achieving satiety. Examples are energy drinks, juice, or soda.

High-Calorie Additions

High-fat salad dressings, shortening and butter add flavor, but they also add large amounts of calories. While on the Optavia diet, it is best to stay away from these additions or replace them with a lower-calorie version.

Indulgent Desserts

You should avoid indulging your sugar cravings with sweets such as ice cream, cookies, or cakes. After you are done with the Optimal Weight 5&1 Plan, you can, then, start consuming moderate sweet treats such as flavored yogurt or fresh fruit.

Foods off Limits

Some foods are not available on the Optimal Weight 5&1 Plan, but they get worked back in once you get to the program's maintenance phase:

- **Whole grain products**: Brown rice, high-fiber cereal, whole-wheat pasta, and whole-grain bread

- **Low-fat dairy products**: Milk, cheese, and yogurt

- **Fruit**: All fruits

- **Starchy Vegetables**: Potatoes, peas, and corns

Chapter 5. **What Advantages Does The Optavia Diet Offer?**

The Optavia diet depends on restrictive dinner substitution items and careful, calorie-controlled arranged suppers, so there's very little space for change.

Extraordinary calorie limitation can cause exhaustion, mind haze, cerebral pains, or menstrual changes. All things considered, the 5&1 alternative ought not to be utilized long haul.

Be that as it may, the 3&3 and 4&2&1 Plans are normally between 1100 and 2500 calories for every day and can gracefully be fitted to use them for a more extended period.

After more than my 1-year journey in doing Optavia Diet, these are the following pros and cons I have noticed:

Pros

Optavia's program may be a solid match for you on the off chance that you need a clear and simple-to-follow diet plan; it will assist you with getting in shape rapidly and offer words for social help.

When embarking on any new diet regimen, you may experience some difficulties along the way. Below are the reasons why this diet regimen is considered the easiest to follow among all commercial diet regimens:

Accomplishes Rapid Weight Loss: Most solid individuals require around 1600 to 3000 calories each day to keep up their weight. Limiting that number to as low as 800 basically ensures weight loss for many people.

Optavia's 5&1 Plan is intended for brisk weight loss, making it a strong choice for somebody with a clinical motivation to shed pounds quickly.

You enter the fat-loss stage in just 3 days. Look for weight-loss stories on "YouTube" to see how many people out there are losing an impressing amount of weight, even 20 or more pounds in a week.

The average of 12 pounds in 12 weeks on the website counts all the people that do it by themselves, and nobody knows how many times they actually follow the plan, how many times they cheat, how much water they drink, exercise, etc.

Easy to follow: As the diet depends on pre-packaged Fuelings generally, you are only accountable for doing one meal a day on the 5&1 Plan.

Moreover, each individual plan comes with meal logs and a sample meal plan to make it easier for the client to follow.

Although you are encouraged to make 1 to 3 Lean and Green foods a day, contingent on the strategy, they are very simple to make—because the program will include detailed recipes and a list of food options for you to choose from.

In addition, those who are not keen on cooking can purchase pre-packaged meals called "Flavors of Home" to substitute for the Lean and Green meals.

In spite of the fact that you should search for your own elements for Lean and Green dinners, the home conveyance choice for Optavia's Fuelings spares time and vitality.

When the items show up, they're anything but difficult to get ready and make phenomenal snatch-and-go suppers.

Packaged products: They will be delivered directly to your home, and they are quick-to-making and grab-and-go.

Social support and Coaching: Stay motivated, do not cheat. Point out how people on coaching achieve a much faster and more massive weight loss.

Offers social help: Social help is a crucial part of achievement with any weight-loss plan. Optavia's training projects and gatherings can give words of consolation and backing for clients.

Optavia's health coaches are available throughout the weight loss and maintenance programs.

It's not a ketogenic diet: Carbs are allowed and higher than the majority of weight-loss diets out there, just not refined ones.

No counting calories: You don't really need to count your calories when following this type of diet, just as long as you stick to the rule of Fuelings, meals, snacks and water intake depending on your preference, may it be 5&1, 4&2&1 or 3&3.

Chapter 6. **What Are The Drawbacks Of An Optavia Diet?**

There are also some potential drawbacks to Optavia's plan, especially if you're concerned about cost, flexibility, and variety:

1. High Monthly Cost

The cost of Optavia can put off some potential users. The 5 & 1 plan price ranges from $350 to $425 for about 120 servings. Also, consider the cost of the food you will need to purchase to prepare your "lean and green" meals. The essential kits, which are the cheapest plan offers, cost more than $300 a month, and that doesn't include what you spend on your lean, green meals.

I present you an estimate of the costs for each plan:

- **5 and 1 Plan**: $390 for approximately 120 servings (30-day supply)

- **4 & 2 & 1 Plan**: $400 for 140 servings (30-day supply)

- **3 and 3 Plan**: $310 for 130 servings (30-day supply)

2. Includes Processed Foods

Although Optavia's "supplies" are designed with interchangeable nutrients, they remain processed foods, which may be a drawback for some users. Some researchers have shown that eating a lot of processed food can have harmful health effects.

3. Fast Recovery of Lost Weight

Additionally, weight loss may not be sustainable. A challenge for anyone on a diet is figuring out how to maintain weight loss once the program is complete.

4. Excessive Calorie Restriction

Although Optavia's diet recommends frequently eating throughout the day, each of its "supplies" provides only 110 calories. Even "lean and green" meals are low in calories. When you eat few calories, you may notice that the plan leaves you hungry and unsatisfied. Additionally, you may also feel more tired and irritable.

5. Boredom and Isolation During Meals

Optavia's dependence on meal replacements can interfere with the social aspects of food preparation and consumption. Users may find it embarrassing or disappointing to make a smoothie during family meals or when dining out with friends.

Compare Optavia with Some Famous Diet

The Optavia diet is beneficial for rapid weight loss compared to other programs due to the low calories provided by its "lean and green" foods and meals. This diet was ranked 31st in the best overall diets with an overall score of 2.7 / 5.

The coaching component of Optavia is comparable to Weight Watchers and Jenny Craig that encourages attendees to opt for meetups to get social support. The processed nature of most of the foods you'll eat on the Optavia diet can be a drawback to the range of fresh and whole foods you can eat with more self-guided plans like the Atkins diet.

Chapter 7. **Meal Planner + Shopping List**

Meal planning becomes simple in the 5 & 1 plan when you know the nutritional parameters of a lean and green meal.

According to your lean protein options, a Lean & Green meal contains 5 to 7 ounces of prepared lean Protein with three portions of vegetables that are not starchy and up to two portions of healthy fats.

Savor your Lean & Green meal — whenever it fits best on your timetable, at any time of day.

If you're eating out or monitoring your consumption, use the Lean & Green Meal Nutritional Criteria given below to better direct your choices:

- Nutritional Criteria of L&G Meal
- Calories 250-400 Calories
- Carbs < 20g of total carbohydrate (ideally < 15 g)
- Protein >= 25g
- Fat 10 – 20g

The three key components of each lean and green meal are Protein, good fats and carbohydrates. The list of ingredients you would need to make a balanced meal and shop according to your meal schedule is provided below.

Protein is classified into the lean, leaner, and leanest types. Purchase groceries according to recipes of your liking and recipe them to your taste.

LEANEST: Pick a 7-oz.

The cooked part, which has 0-4gof net fat, then includes 2 healthy fat servings.

Fish: cod, haddock, flounder, rough orange, tilapia, grouper, haddock, Mahi Mahi, wild catfish, tuna canned in water)

Shellfish: scallops, crab, lobster, shrimp

Game meat: buffalo, deer, elk

Turkey (Ground) or other meat: around 98% lean.

Meatless choices:

- 14 whites of eggs
- 2 cups of liquid egg white or liquid egg replacement
- 5 oz. seitan
- 11/2 cups or 2 oz. of 1% cottage cheese
- 12 ounces of Non-fat (0%) regular Greek yogurt (approximately 15gcarb per 12 ounces.)

LEANER: Pick a 6 oz. The part cooked, which has 5-9gof net fat and includes 1 portion of Healthy Fat.

Fish species: swordfish,

Halibut, trout,

White meat or Chicken breast skin-free

Turkey (Ground) or other poultry: 95%-97% lean meat.

Turkey: light poultry

Meatless choices:

- Two entire eggs or four egg whites
- Two entire eggs and one cup of liquid egg replacer
- 1 1/2 cups or 12 oz. or
- 2% cottage cheese
- 12 ounces. Low fat (2%) regular Greek yogurt (approximately 15gcarb per 12 ounces.

LEAN: Pick a part of 5 oz. Cooked with 10g-20g net fat-no extra portion of healthy fat.

Fish: tuna (bluefin steak), salmon, catfish farmed, herring, mackerel

Lean beef: roasted, ground, steak

Lamb

Pork fillet or Pork chop

Turkey (Ground) or other poultry: 85%-94% leaner meat.

Turkey or chicken: dark meat

Meatless choices:

- 15 ounces. Extra-firm or firm (bean curd) tofu
- Three eggs whole (up to 2 days a week)
- 4 ounces. part-skim cheese or Reduced-fat (3-6g fat per ounce) (1 cup shredded)
- 8 ounces. (1 cup) ricotta part-skim cheese (2-3gof fat per ounce.)
- 5-ounces   Tempe

Healthy Amounts of Fat

There can be around 5gof fat and less than

5gof carb in a portion of healthy fat. Include 0-2 Healthy Fat Portions daily

Depending on your options for Lean:

- 1 tsp of oil (any sort)
- 1 tbsp of normal, low-carb dressing for the salad
- 2 tbsp lowered-fat, low-carb dressing for the salad
- 5-10 green or black olives
- 1 1/2 ounce. Avocado
- 1/3 ounce. Simple nuts, such as almonds, pistachios, or peanuts
- 1 tbsp of simple seeds, such as sesame, flax, chia, or Seeds of pumpkin
- 1/2 tbsp Regular margarine, butter, or mayonnaise

Green & Lean Meal: The "Greens"

Greens make up a substantial proportion of the carbohydrates eaten in the 5 & 1 diet.

Pick three servings from our Green Choices collection for each of your meals (Lean & Green). We've sorted the choices for vegetables into the amounts of lower, medium and higher carb levels. Every one of them is acceptable on the Optimum Weight 5 & 1 meal plan; the list assists you to make responsible choices on food.

From the Green Choice List, pick 3 servings:

1 serving = 1/2 cup (except where specified) of vegetables with Around 25 calories and around 5gof carbohydrates

LOW CARB

1 cup: endive, green leaf lettuce, Butterhead, romaine, iceberg, collard (fresh/raw), spinach (fresh/raw), mustard greens, watercress, bok choy (raw), spring mix

1/2 cup: cucumbers, radishes, white mushrooms, sprouts (Mung bean, alfalfa), turnip greens, celery, arugula, escarole, Swiss chard (raw), jalapeño (raw), bok choy (cooked), nopales,

MODERATE CARB

1/2 cup: cabbage, eggplant, cauliflower, fennel bulb, asparagus, Mushrooms, Kale, portabella, summer squash (scallop or zucchini) cooked spinach,

HIGHER CARB

1/2 cup: red cabbage, squash, collard, chayote squash(cooked) mustard greens, green or wax beans, broccoli, kabocha squash, (cooked) leeks, Kohlrabi, okra, (any color) peppers, scallions (raw), (crookneck or straightneck) summer squash, Turnips, Tomatoes, Spaghetti Squash, Palm Cores, Jicama, Swiss (cooked) chard

Sample Meal Plan

The meal plan of the optimal 5 & 1 program is very easy and simple to follow:

The fuelings are readily available in a pre-packaged and ready-to-eat form.

The only prep you need is for a lean and green meal, which is also made easy for you by providing you with easy recipes and a grocery list a sample meal plan is provided to help you understand the simplicity of this weight-loss program.

A Day in the Optimal 5&1 plan

Fueling 1 ex: Caramel Mocha Shake

Fueling 2 ex: Creamy Double Crisp Peanut Butter Bar

Fueling 3 ex: Roasted Creamy Garlic Smashed Potatoes

Fueling 4 ex: Cinnamon Sugary Sticks

Fueling 5 ex: Chewy Dewy Chocolate Chip Biscuit

Lean & Green Meal (your favorite recipe from this book) Water Intake (check off how many glasses of water you have each day) = 8 oz.

__ 8

__ 15

__ 21

__ 26

Chapter 8. **Fueling Recipes**

1. Smooth Peanut Butter Cream

Preparation Time: 10 minutes

Cooking Time: 0 minutes

Servings: 8

Ingredients:

- ¼ cup peanut butter
- 4 overripe bananas, chopped
- 1/3 cup cocoa powder
- 1/3 tsp. vanilla extract
- 1/8 tsp. salt

Directions:

1. In the blender, add all the listed ingredients and blend until smooth.
2. Serve immediately and enjoy.

Nutrition:

Calories: 101 kcal

Fats: 5g

Carbs: 14g

Protein: 3g

Sugar: 7g

Cholesterol: 0mg

2. Peanut Butter Crunch Bars

Preparation Time: 20 min. + chilling

Cooking Time: 0 minutes

Servings: 3

Ingredients:

- 3 cups miniature pretzels, coarsely chopped
- 10 tbsp butter, divided
- 1 package (10 ounces) miniature marshmallows
- 3 cups Rice Krispies
- 1/2 cup light corn syrup, divided
- 3/4 cup peanut butter chips
- 1 cup semisweet chocolate chips
- 1/4 cup dry roasted peanuts, chopped

Direction:

1. Reserve 1/3 cup chopped pretzels. In a large microwave-safe bowl, microwave 6 tablespoons butter on high for 45-60 seconds or until melted. Stir in marshmallows; cook 1 to 1-1/2 minutes or until

marshmallows are melted, stirring every 30 seconds. Stir in Rice Krispies and remaining chopped pretzels. Immediately press into a greased 13x9-in. baking pan.

2. In another microwave-safe bowl, combine 2 tablespoons butter and 1/4 cup corn syrup. Microwave, uncovered, on high for 45-60 seconds or until butter is melted, stirring once. Add peanut butter chips; cook 30-40 seconds or until chips are melted, stirring once. Spread over cereal layer.

3. In a microwave-safe bowl, combine the remaining corn syrup and remaining butter. Cook on high for 45-60 seconds or until butter is melted, stirring once. Add chocolate chips; cook 30-40 seconds longer or until chips are melted, stirring once. Spread over top.

4. Sprinkle with peanuts and reserved pretzels; press down gently. Cover and refrigerate for 30 minutes or until set. Cut into bars. Store in airtight containers.

Nutrition:

Calories: 136 (per bar)

Fat: 6g (3g saturated fat)

Cholesterol: 8mg

Sodium: 124mg

Carbohydrate: 20g (10g sugars, 1g fiber)

Protein: 2g

3. Chocolate Crunch Cookies

Preparation Time: 20 min. + chilling

Cooking Time: 0 minutes

Servings: 3

Ingredients:

Caramelized Krispies

- 1/2 cup butter
- 1/4 cup granulated sugar
- 2 cups rice Krispy cereal
- pinch of salt

Cookies

- 1 cup cold butter, cubed
- 1 cup light brown sugar

- 1/2 cup granulated sugar
- 2 eggs
- 1 tsp vanilla
- 1/2 cup cocoa powder
- 3/4 tsp baking soda
- 3/4 tsp kosher salt
- 2 1/2 cups all-purpose flour
- 2 cups Nestle "Buncha Crunch" or chopped Nestle Crunch Bars

Directions:

Caramelized Krispies

1. In a medium nonstick skillet over medium heat melt the butter and sugar together, stirring frequently. Add the cereal and salt and stir to coat. Continue stirring often, until the cereal is an amber color, 5 – 10 minutes.
2. Transfer to a parchment-lined counter or baking sheet to cool.

Cookies

1. Preheat oven to 350°F. Line a baking sheet with parchment paper and set it aside.
2. In the bowl of your stand mixer fitted with the paddle attachment mix the butter cubes until it's smooth, about 1 minute. Add in both sugars and continue mixing on medium speed for 2 more minutes until light and fluffy, scraping the sides of your bowl as necessary.
3. Next, add in the cocoa powder until evenly mixed.
4. With the mixer still on medium add in the eggs, vanilla, baking soda and salt and mix for 1 minute until smooth, scraping the sides of the bowl making sure everything is incorporated.
5. Turn the mixer to low and add in the flour, mixing until just combined.
6. Stir in your "Buncha Crunch" or chopped Crunch Bars, and Caramelized Krispies until incorporated.
7. Using a large (3 tbsp) cookie scoop drop the dough onto the prepared cookie sheet.
8. Bake for 9-11 minutes until the edges are set. Centers might seem under-cooked, this is ok.
9. Allow the cookies to cool for 3 minutes on the cookie sheet and transfer to a wire rack to cool completely.

Nutrition:

Calories: 2457 kcal

Fats: 136.85g

Carbs: 297.04g

Protein: 28.15g

Sugar: 176.52g

Cholesterol: 673mg

4. Brownie Ice Cream Sandwiches

Preparation Time: 1 hour

Cooking Time: 30 minutes

Servings: 8-12

Ingredients:

- 1 cup (2 sticks; 230g) unsalted butter
- 2 cups (400g) granulated sugar
- 3 large eggs, at room temperature
- 1 tbsp pure vanilla extract
- 1 cup (85g) unsweetened natural or Dutch-process cocoa powder
- 1 cup (125g) all-purpose flour (spoon & leveled)
- 1 tsp salt
- 3/4 tsp baking powder
- 2-quart container (1/2 gallon) vanilla ice cream (slightly softened– you can use any flavor and you'll have a little leftover)

Directions:

Preliminary note: For best success, I recommend reviewing the recipe notes and video tutorial above before beginning.

1. Preheat the oven to 350°F (177°C) and line a 9-inch square baking pan with parchment paper, leaving enough overhang on the sides to lift the warm brownies out. Set aside. (If you have 2 identical 9-inch square baking pans, you can line both and bake the batches of brownie batter at the same time.) I don't recommend other size baking pans. See my recipe note.

2. In a microwave-safe bowl or a saucepan on the stove, melt the butter. After melting, whisk in the sugar until completely combined, then whisk in the eggs and vanilla. The batter will be a little dull looking.

3. Add the cocoa powder, flour, salt, and baking powder. Fold it all together with a rubber spatula or wooden spoon. It will come together, I promise! The batter will be very thick. You will have about 4 cups of batter.

4. Spoon and spread half of the batter (about 2 cups) into the prepared pan. (Lightly cover the remaining batter and keep at room temperature.) The batter is thick and heavy, so do your best to spread it evenly in the lined baking pan. I find the back of a spoon is most helpful. Place a small sheet of parchment paper directly on top of the brownie batter, smoothing it down as pictured in the photos and video tutorial above. The top parchment paper helps the brownies stay flat and prevents the brownies from puffing up too much.

5. Bake for 15-16 minutes. I find any longer over-cooks the brownies, making the ice cream sandwiches difficult to cut and eat. Remove brownies from the oven and cool for 5 minutes in the pan. Carefully, using the overhanging parchment paper on the sides, lift the warm and soft square sheet of brownies out of the pan as a whole. Remove the top piece of parchment. (You can reuse it for the top of the 2nd sheet of brownies in the next step if desired.) Set aside.

6. Line the warm pan with another sheet of parchment paper, leaving enough overhang on the sides to lift the warm brownies out. Give the remaining brownie batter a stir. It will be very thick at this point. Add a tsp of water to thin out if necessary. (No more.) Spoon and spread the remaining brownie batter in the pan. Place a small sheet of parchment paper directly on top of the brownie batter, just as you did before.

7. Bake for 15-16 minutes. Remove brownies from the oven and cool for 15 minutes in the pan. During this cooling time, I remove the ice cream from the freezer so it has a chance to soften.

8. Scoop the softened ice cream onto the warm brownie layer in the pan. You'll use almost all of the 1/2 gallon of ice cream. Using the back of a spoon or your ice cream scoop, gently spread it into an even and thick layer.

9. Carefully pick up the 1st square sheet of brownies and place them on top of the ice cream layer. Gently press it down into the ice cream to help it stick. Cover the entire pan with aluminum foil or plastic wrap and freeze for at least 12 hours and up to 1 week. I find 12-18 hours is the perfect amount of time. Any

less and the ice cream will still be pretty soft. The longer after 18 hours, the harder the sandwiches are to cut.

10. Remove the pan of ice cream brownies from the freezer. Carefully lift them out as a whole using the parchment paper overhang on the sides. Using a very sharp knife and some arm muscle, cut into 8-12 squares or rectangles. Enjoy immediately.

11. Wrap each leftover sandwich individually and store it in the freezer for up to 1 month. They get a little harder the longer they sit in the freezer– if they're super solid, let them sit out for a few minutes before enjoying.

Nutrition:

Calories: 228 kcal

Fats: 12.45g

Carbs: 29.05g

Protein: 3.66g

Sugar: 16.62g

Cholesterol: 66 mg

5. Grilled Cheese Tomato Sandwich

Preparation Time: 15 minutes

Cooking Time: 8 minutes

Servings: 2

Ingredients:

- 4 slices sourdough bread
- 2 tbsp mayonnaise
- 1 large tomato sliced
- 2 ounces cheddar cheese sliced
- 2 ounces gruyere cheese or mozzarella, grated
- pinch of dried basil

Direction

1. Slice tomato ¼" thick and sprinkle with 1/4 tsp salt. Place on paper towels and let drain 10 minutes.
2. Spread mayonnaise over the outside of each slice of bread.

3. Place 1 slice of cheddar on each slice of bread. Add tomato slices and basil. Top with gruyere and remaining slice of bread.

4. Preheat a small skillet over low heat. Place mayonnaise side down in the skillet.

5. Grill until golden, about 4-5 minutes. Flip and grill the other side until golden.

Nutrition:

Calories: 731 kcal

Carbohydrates: 76g

Protein: 32g

Fat: 34g

Saturated Fat: 15g

Cholesterol: 72mg

Sodium: 1039mg

Potassium: 430mg

Fiber: 4g

6. Slutty Brownie

Preparation Time: 10 minutes

Cooking Time: 40 minutes

Servings: 16

Ingredients:

For the Brownie layer:

- 10 tbsp unsalted butter
- 1 1/4 cups white sugar
- 3/4 cup cocoa powder
- 1/2 tsp kosher salt
- 2 tsp vanilla extract

- 2 large eggs
- 1/2 cup flour

For the Oreo layer:

- 1 package of Oreo regular stuffed or double stuffed

For the Cookie Dough layer:

- 1/2 cup unsalted butter at room temp
- 1/4 cup brown sugar
- 3/4 cup white sugar
- 1 egg
- 1 1/4 tsp vanilla extract
- 1 1/4 cups flour
- 1/2 tsp salt
- 1/2 tsp baking soda
- 1/2 tsp baking powder
- 1 cup semi-sweet chocolate chips

Directions:

For the Brownie layer:

1. In a medium saucepan, melt the butter over medium-high heat. Add the sugar and cocoa powder once the butter is melted. Whisk to combine and remove from heat. Add the salt, vanilla and eggs, and continuously whisk until the eggs are combined. Add the flour and continue to mix. Set batter aside.

For the Cookie Dough layer:

1. Cream together the butter and sugars in a mixer. Add the egg and vanilla, making sure to scrape down the sides of the mixing bowl. Add the flour, salt, baking soda and baking powder and mix on low until everything is incorporated. Fold in the chocolate chips. Set dough aside.
2. Line the bottom of a 9x9 baking pan with tin foil and then spray the tin foil with a layer of baking spray.
3. Layer the cookie dough on the bottom of a 9x9 baking pan, pressing down to form the bottom of the slutty brownies.
4. Layer as many Oreos that will fit on top of the cookie dough. No need to overlap. One single layer will do.
5. Pour the brownie batter on top of the Oreo layer and make sure it's evenly layered on top.

6. Bake for 30-40 minutes. Test with a knife to see if the center is done. If the knife comes out clean, let the brownies rest for at least 2 hours before serving. If the knife comes out with batter still on it, allow the brownies to bake about 5 minutes more. Slice and serve.

Nutrition:

Calories: 229 kcal

Carbohydrates: 27.6g

Protein: 3.43g

Fat: 12.6g

Saturated Fat: 15g

Cholesterol: 86 mg

7. Chocolate Chip Cakes

Preparation Time: 10 minutes

Cooking Time: 35 minutes

Servings: 12

Ingredients:

Cake Batter:

- 2 cups (10 ounces) all-purpose flour
- 1 1/2 cups (11.25 ounces) granulated sugar
- 2 tsp baking powder
- 1/2 tsp baking soda

- 1/2 tsp salt
- 1 1/3 cups sour cream
- 10 tbsp (5 ounces) butter, softened
- 3 eggs
- 1 tsp vanilla

Cinnamon + Sugar + Chocolate:

- 1/4 cup granulated sugar
- 2 tsp ground cinnamon
- 2 cups (12 ounces) chocolate chips, regular or mini (see note)

Direction:

1. Preheat the oven to 350 degrees (325 if using a glass pan). Grease a 9 X 13 pan with cooking spray and/or line with parchment paper for easier cleanup.
2. In the bowl of a stand mixer fitted with the paddle attachment or in a large bowl using an electric handheld mixer, combine all of the cake batter ingredients. Mix until well-combined, about 2 minutes.
3. Whisk together the cinnamon and sugar until combined.
4. Spread half of the batter in the bottom of the prepared pan. Sprinkle with half of the cinnamon sugar and then sprinkle half of the chocolate chips over the top.
5. Spoon the remaining cake batter on top in large dollops and spread evenly to cover. Sprinkle with the remaining cinnamon and sugar and chocolate chips.
6. Bake for 30-35 minutes until golden on top and set around the edges and a toothpick comes out with only a few moist crumbs (don't over bake or the cake will be dry!). Serve warm or at room temperature.

Nutrition:

Calories: 506 kcal

Carbohydrates: 82.75g

Protein: 7.98g

Fat: 15.82g

Saturated Fat: 8.8g

Cholesterol: 189 mg

8. Pudding Pies

Preparation Time: 20 minutes

Cooking Time: 0 minutes

Servings: 9

Ingredients:

Crust

- 1 & 1/2 cups graham cracker crumbs (about 9 graham crackers)
- 1/4 cup brown sugar
- 6 tbsp unsalted melted butter

Filling

- 2– 3.4 oz (or 3.9) instant chocolate pudding mix
- 3 cups heavy cream
- 1 container cool whip (8 oz) thawed

Topping

- 1 cup heavy cream
- 1/4 cup powdered sugar
- 1 tsp vanilla extract

Direction:

Crust

1. In a large bowl, combine the graham cracker crumbs, brown sugar and melted butter. Press this mixture evenly into a 9- or 10-inch pie pan. Use the bottom of a measuring cup to pack the crust down. Place the crust in the fridge to chill until ready to fill.

Filling

1. In a stand mixer or large mixing bowl, combine the pudding mix and heavy cream with an electric mixer until well blended. You will NOT prepare the pudding mix as directed on the box. If you have a stand mixer, this is a great time to use it because when you beat the pudding mix and heavy cream together, the mixture will be very thick.
2. Add the cool whip and mix on low until combined. Spread this mixture over the crust. Once you add in the cool whip, the mixture will become creamier and fluffier. Cover the pie pan with plastic wrap and refrigerate for 4-8 hours.

Topping

1. Before serving the pie - place a metal or glass mixing bowl and beaters in the freezer for 15 minutes.
2. Remove the bowl from the freezer. Add the heavy cream, powdered sugar and vanilla extract and beat with an electric mixer for 4-5 minutes, or until stiff peaks form / it's scoop-able with a spoon and holds its shape.
3. Spoon onto the pie and top with chocolate shavings.

Nutrition:

Calories: 394 kcal

Fats: 30.75g

Carbs: 27.41g

Protein: 3.01g

9. Chocolate Coconut Cake

Preparation Time: 1 hour 5 minutes

Cooking Time: 45 minutes

Servings: 24

Ingredients:

For The Cake

- 2 ½ cups (325 g) all-purpose flour
- 1 tsp baking soda
- ½ tsp salt
- 4 ounces (113 g) semisweet chocolate, finely chopped
- 1 cup (226 g) unsalted butter, softened
- 2 cups (400g) granulated sugar
- 4 large eggs
- 1 tsp vanilla extract
- 2/3 cup (56 g) unsweetened cocoa powder, plus more for dusting the pan
- 1 ½ cups (360 ml) canned coconut milk

For The Filling

- 1 cup (240 ml) canned coconut milk
- 4 large egg yolks
- 1/3 cup (67 g) granulated sugar
- 2 ½ tbsp cornstarch
- 1 tsp coconut extract
- 2 tbsp unsalted butter, cut into pieces
- ½ cup (43 g) shredded sweetened coconut

For The Frosting

- 1 recipe coconut buttercream frosting

For The Glaze

- 4 ounces (113 g) semisweet chocolate, coarsely chopped

- 4 tbsp unsalted butter, cut into pieces
- 2 tbsp light corn syrup
- ½ to 1 cup (43-85 g) shredded sweetened coconut

Direction:

Make the Cake

1. Heat the oven to 325°F. Spray 3 8-inch round pans with nonstick spray. Line the bottoms with parchment paper cut into a circle to fit the pan. Spray the parchment paper with nonstick spray and dust the pan lightly with cocoa powder. Tap out any excess and set aside.
2. In a medium bowl, combine the flour, baking soda and salt. Stir with a whisk and set aside.
3. Add the chocolate to a small heatproof bowl and set it over a pot of barely simmering water. Stir continuously until melted and smooth. Remove from heat. Set aside to cool.
4. Using a stand mixer fitted with a paddle attachment or a handheld electric mixer beat the butter and sugar together on medium-low speed until light and fluffy. Beat in the eggs, one at a time, mixing well after each addition. Scrape down the sides of the bowl as needed. Beat in the vanilla. Add the cocoa powder and melted chocolate and mix until well incorporated. With the mixer set to low speed, gradually add half the flour mixture, followed by the coconut milk, and then the remaining flour mixture. Beat just until combined. The batter will be thick.
5. Divide the batter evenly between the 3 prepared pans. Use an offset spatula to spread the batter all the way to the edges of the pan and smooth out the surface. Bake for 28 to 30 minutes, or until a toothpick inserted into the center comes out with only a few dry crumbs. Cool the cake in the pans for 10 minutes, then invert the cakes onto a wire rack to cool completely. Peel the parchment paper off the bottoms before filling.

Make the Filling

1. Bring the coconut milk up to a simmer in a medium saucepan. In a separate bowl, whisk the egg yolks, sugar, cornstarch, and extract until blended and pale in color. Slowly pour in the hot milk while whisking continuously. Return the mixture back to the pot and whisk over medium-high heat until thickened, about 3 minutes. Pour the thickened pastry cream through a fine-mesh sieve then stir in the butter until fully melted. Place a piece of plastic wrap directly on top of the pastry cream, making sure it is touching the surface, and refrigerate until cooled completely. Stir in the shredded coconut.
2. Place one of the cake layers on a serving plate, bottom side up. Spread half the pastry cream over the top, leaving a ½-inch margin around the edge. Top with another cake layer. Repeat with remaining pastry cream and top with the third cake layer.

Make the Frosting

1. Prepare the coconut buttercream frosting according to the recipe instructions. Spread the frosting over the top and sides of the cake. Using a large cake scraper, remove frosting from the sides of the cake until the cake layers begin to show through.

Make the Glaze

1. Place the chocolate, butter, and corn syrup in a medium heatproof bowl set over a pot of barely simmering water. Stir until melted and smooth. Remove from heat and let cool for 5 minutes.
2. Spoon ¼ cup of the chocolate glaze over the top of the cake. Drizzle the remaining glaze along the edge of the cake all the way around, allowing it to drip down the sides. Sprinkle shredded coconut over the top.

Notes

Make-Ahead Tip

Wrap baked and cooled cake layers tightly in plastic wrap and store them in the refrigerator. Assemble and frost the cake within 2 days. Or layers can be triple wrapped in plastic wrap and frozen for up to 2 weeks. Leave wrapped and set on the counter to thaw slightly before use.

The frosting and filling can be prepared, covered and refrigerated for up to 1 day before use.

Once the cake has been assembled, cover it and keep it stored in the refrigerator for up to three days. Bring it to room temperature just before serving.

The frosted cake can be frozen for up to 2 months. Thaw it overnight in the refrigerator and let it come to room temperature just before serving

Nutrition:

Calories: 291 kcal

Fats: 13.23g

Carbs: 40.04g

Protein: 4.83g

10.Sweet Potato Protein Pancakes

Preparation Time: 10 minutes

Cooking Time: 10 minutes

Servings: 2

Ingredients:

- 1 large sweet potato (about a cup mashed)
- 1 cup liquid egg whites
- 1 scoop vanilla protein powder (I used whey)
- 1/4 cup ground flaxseed
- 1/2 tsp baking powder
- cinnamon to taste
- 1/2 tsp vanilla

Directions:

1. Combine all ingredients in a blender and blend till smooth, about 30 seconds to a minute.

2. Cook pancakes on medium heat, flipping after 30 seconds to a minute.

Nutrition:

Calories: 230 kcal

Carbohydrates: 11g

Protein: 25g

Fat: 9g

Saturated Fat: 1g

Cholesterol: 30mg

11.Mexican Meatloaf

Preparation Time: 30 minutes

Cooking Time: 55 minutes

Servings: 6-8

Ingredients:

Meatloaf:

- 2 tbsp olive oil
- 1/2 cup finely chopped onion
- 1 medium carrot, finely chopped
- 1 rib finely chopped celery
- 1 clove of garlic, minced
- 1-pound ground beef
- 6 ounces soft Mexican chorizo, removed from casing and crumbled
- 1 poblano chile, roasted, peeled and diced
- 3/4 tsp salt
- 1/4 tsp freshly ground black pepper
- 1/4 tsp cayenne pepper
- 1/2 tsp ground cumin
- 2 eggs, well beaten
- 1/4 cup ketchup
- 1/4 cup sour cream or Mexican sour cream
- 1/2 cup dried bread crumbs

Salsa-Glaze:

- 2 medium tomatoes, cored
- 1/4 medium white onion
- 2 cloves of garlic, unpeeled
- 1 to 3 serrano chiles
- 1/4 cup brown sugar
- 1 canned chipotle chile in adobo sauce, minced
- 1 tbsp yellow mustard

- Kosher salt

Direction:

1. Preheat the oven to 375 degrees F.
2. In a heavy skillet, add the oil and heat over medium-high heat. Add the onion, carrot, celery, and garlic. Cook, stirring often until vegetables are soft, about 8 minutes. Set aside until cool enough to handle.
3. In a large bowl combine the sauteed vegetables, ground beef, chorizo and diced poblano chile.
4. In a medium bowl, combine the salt, pepper, cayenne, cumin and eggs. Add the ketchup and sour cream. Mix well with a fork and pour it on top of the mixed meats. Sprinkle with bread crumbs and mix thoroughly with clean hands.
5. Put the mixture into a 9 by 13-inch loaf-pan. Bake until an instant-read thermometer inserted into the center of the meatloaf registers 160 degrees F, about 40 to 45 minutes. Remove from the oven and carefully pour off any accumulated pan juices.
6. Meanwhile, heat a heavy skillet over high heat. Add the whole tomatoes, onion, garlic cloves, and serrano chiles. Cook, turning frequently until lightly charred on all sides. Peel the garlic cloves. Add all the charred ingredients to a blender. Pulse until chunky, then pour into a small skillet. Stir in the sugar, chipotle chile and mustard. Bring the mixture to a boil over medium heat. Cook until slightly thickened, about 4 to 5 minutes. Season with salt, to taste.
7. Slice the meatloaf and arrange it on a platter. Spoon the salsa-glaze over the meatloaf and serve.

Nutrition:

Calories: 287 kcal

Fats: 15.69g

Carbs: 14.7g

Protein: 21.5g

Chapter 9. **Chicken Recipes**

12. Tender Taco Chicken

Preparation Time: 5 Minutes

Cooking Time: 10 Minutes

Servings: 4 Servings. 6 ounces of chicken is the serving amount. You should classify it as .25 Green, or one condiment— because of the minimal number of tomatoes used.

Ingredients

- 1 tbsp. Dash of Desperation Seasoning
- 1/2 C fresh chopped tomatoes or low carb, no sugar added salsa
- 1 Tbsp Phoenix Sunrise Seasoning or Southwestern Seasoning (or your favorite low carb, low salt Tex-Mex seasoning)

- 1 1/2 pounds boneless, skinless chicken breast
- Your favorite on-program taco condiments

Directions:

1. Rinse the chicken and add it to the Instapot middle. Set in a thin layer (some overlapping is all right)
2. Toss the Phoenix Sunrise Seasoning and the Dash of Desperation with the chicken.
3. Using a spoon to spread it equally, pour the tomatoes or sauce over the chicken.
4. On the Instapot, put the lid and close the lid and make sure that the release valve is in the lock's location.
5. Cook for 9 minutes at a high temperature and then use the fast release process to reduce the steam.
6. Remove the chicken and use two forks to shred it.
7. For added spice, you can use the liquid at the bottom of the Instapot as a sauce over the chicken. Only spill it over the chicken that has been shredded. You should move your Instapot to the Sauté setting if there is too much fluid and let it simmer for 3-5 minutes before the liquid is decreased by 1/2. Then pour the thick sauce over the chicken and enjoy with your favorite taco toppings!

Nutrition:

Calories 325 kcal

Fat 10.46g

Protein 16.44g

Carbohydrate 40.42g

13.Basil Chicken Sausage & Zucchini Spaghetti

Preparation Time: 10 Minutes

Cooking Time: 15 Minutes

Servings: 4 serving— 1/4 of this recipe is the serving size.

Ingredients

- 8 tbsp fresh grated Parmesan Cheese
- 2 cup tomato sauce- no sugar added
- 1 tbsp Tuscan Fantasy Seasoning (or bell pepper, black pepper, garlic, onion, parsley, salt)
- 1 1/2 pounds (24 oz.) lean chicken sausage (you can also use turkey sausage or beef sausage— pay attention to portion sizes for different meats)
- 4 cup spiraled zucchini

Directions:

1. Break the sausage into 1/2-inch chunks.
2. Over medium-high heat, put a large frying pan (at least 1 1/2 "deep).
3. Add the chicken to the frying pan and cook until the sausage is finely browned, stirring regularly, for 7-8 minutes.
4. To cover the chicken, add the tomato sauce & Tuscan Fantasy into the pan and stir. Turn the fire up to high and get the sauce to a boil for a moment. (approximately 3 more minutes)
5. Using a pair of tongs to add the zucchini noodles to the plate throw the noodles in the sauce and cook for just 1-2 minutes until the noodles are tender and the chicken is cooked thoroughly.
6. Place four equal portions on plates and sprinkle with 2 T of Parmesan cheese on each plate. Serve it warm.

Nutrition:

Calories 645 kcal

Fat 52.95g

Protein 24.27g

Carbohydrate 19.57g

14.Orange Chicken

Preparation Time: 40 Minutes

Cooking Time: 40 Minutes

Servings: 4

Ingredients

Sauce:

- 1 1/2 cups water
- 2 tbsp orange juice
- ¼ cup lemon juice
- 1/3 cup rice vinegar
- 2 1/2 tbsp soy sauce
- 1 tbsp grated orange zest
- 1 cup packed brown sugar
- ½ tsp minced fresh ginger root
- ½ tsp minced garlic
- 2 tbsp chopped green onion
- ¼ tsp red pepper flakes
- 3 tbsp cornstarch
- 2 tbsp water

Chicken:

- 2 boneless, skinless chicken breasts, cut into 1/2-inch pieces
- 1 cup all-purpose flour
- ¼ tsp salt
- ¼ tsp pepper
- 3 tbsp olive oil

Direction

1. Pour 1 1/2 cups water, orange juice, lemon juice, rice vinegar and soy sauce into a saucepan and set over medium-high heat. Stir in the orange zest, brown sugar, ginger, garlic, chopped onion and red pepper flakes. Bring to a boil. Remove from heat, and cool 10 to 15 minutes.

2. Place the chicken pieces into a resealable plastic bag. When contents of saucepan have cooled, pour 1 cup of sauce into bag. Reserve the remaining sauce. Seal the bag, and refrigerate for at least 2 hours.

3. In another resealable plastic bag, mix the flour, salt, and pepper. Add the marinated chicken pieces, seal the bag, and shake to coat.

4. Heat the olive oil in a large skillet over medium heat. Place chicken into the skillet, and brown on both sides. Drain on a plate lined with paper towels, and cover with aluminum foil.

5. Wipe out the skillet, and add the sauce. Bring to a boil over medium-high heat. Mix together the cornstarch and 2 tbsp water; stir into the sauce. Reduce heat to medium-low. Add the chicken pieces, and simmer, about 5 minutes, stirring occasionally.

Nutrition:

Calories: 647 kcal

Protein: 53.83g

Carbohydrates: 61.01g

Fat: 19.36g

Cholesterol: 158mg

Sodium: 484mg

15.Spinach and Mushroom Stuffed Chicken

Preparation Time: 15 Minutes

Cooking Time: 20 Minutes

Servings: 4

Ingredients

- 4 boneless, skinless chicken breasts— 6 ounces
- Large plastic food storage bags or waxed paper
- 1 package, 10 ounces, frozen chopped spinach
- 2 tbsp butter
- 12 small mushroom caps, crimini or button
- 2 cloves of garlic, cracked
- 1 small shallot, quartered
- Salt and freshly ground black pepper
- 1 cup part-skim ricotta cheese
- 1/2 cup grated Parmigiano or Romano, a couple of handfuls
- 1/2 tsp fresh grated or ground nutmeg

Toothpicks

- 2 tbsp extra-virgin olive oil

Sauce:

- 2 tbsp butter
- 2 tbsp flour
- 1/2 cup white wine
- 1 cup chicken broth

Direction:

1. Place breasts in the center of a plastic food storage bag or 2 large sheets of waxed paper. Pound out the chicken from the center of the bag outward using a heavy-bottomed skillet or mallet. Be firm but controlled with your strokes.
2. Defrost spinach in the microwave. Transfer spinach to a kitchen towel. Twist towel around spinach and wring it out until very dry. Transfer to a medium mixing bowl.

3. Place a nonstick skillet over moderate heat. When the skillet is hot, add butter, mushrooms, garlic and shallot. Season with salt and pepper and saute for 5 minutes. Transfer mushrooms, garlic and shallot to the food processor. Pulse to grind the mushrooms and transfer to the mixing bowl, adding the processed mushrooms to the spinach. Add ricotta and grated cheese to the bowl and the nutmeg. Stir to combine the stuffing. Return your skillet to the stove over medium-high heat.

4. Place a mound of stuffing on each breast and wrap and roll breast over the stuffing. Secure breasts with toothpicks. Add 3 tbsp of oil to the pan, 3 turns of the pan. Add breasts to the pan and brown on all sides, cooking chicken for 10 to 12 minutes. The meat will cook quickly because it is thin. Remove breasts; add butter to the pan and flour. Cook butter and flour for a minute, whisk in wine and reduce another minute. Whisk in broth and return breasts to the pan. Reduce heat and simmer until ready to serve. Remove toothpicks. Serve breasts whole or— remove from pan— slice on an angle and fan out on dinner plates. Top stuffed chicken breasts or sliced stuffed breasts with generous spoonfuls of the sauce.

Nutrition:

Calories: 339 kcal

Protein: 22.03g

Carbohydrates: 8.93g

Fat: 19.36g

Cholesterol: 158mg

Sodium: 484mg

16.Rosemary Chicken

Preparation Time: 5 Minutes

Cooking Time: 35 Minutes

Servings: 4

Ingredients

- 1 1/4 pounds boneless skinless chicken breasts
- 1 tbsp olive oil
- salt and pepper to taste
- 2 tsp fresh rosemary leaves minced

- 3 tbsp butter melted
- 1 1/4 tsp minced garlic
- 1/4 cup chicken broth
- 2 tbsp lemon juice
- 1 tbsp chopped fresh parsley
- lemon slices and rosemary sprigs for serving optional
- cooking spray

Direction:

1. Preheat the oven to 400 degrees F. Season the chicken breasts generously on both sides with salt and pepper.
2. Heat the olive oil in a large pan over medium-high heat. Add the chicken breasts and cook for 3-5 minutes on each side or until browned.
3. Transfer the chicken to a baking dish coated with cooking spray.
4. In a small bowl, mix together the rosemary, butter, garlic, chicken broth and lemon juice. Pour the butter mixture over the chicken.
5. Bake for 25 minutes or until chicken is cooked through. Bake time may vary depending on the thickness of your chicken breasts. The chicken is done when it reads at least 165 degrees F on a meat thermometer.
6. Spoon the sauce on the bottom of the baking dish over the chicken, then sprinkle with parsley and serve. Garnish with lemon slices and rosemary sprigs if desired.

Nutrition:

Calories: 271 kcal

Protein: 30g

Fat: 15g

Saturated Fat: 6g

Cholesterol: 113mg

17.Stuffed Chicken Breasts with Tomato Salad

Preparation Time: 20 Minutes

Cooking Time: 15 Minutes

Servings: 4

Ingredients

- 1 6.5-ounce jar artichoke hearts, drained and chopped
- 2 tbsp grated Parmesan
- 2 tbsp fresh thyme leaves
- 4–6-ounces boneless, skinless chicken breasts
- 2 tbsp plus 1 tsp extra-virgin olive oil
- kosher salt and pepper
- 2 beefsteak tomatoes, cut into bite-size pieces
- 1 shallot, thinly sliced
- 1 tbsp red wine vinegar
- 8 baguette slices, toasted (optional)

Directions

1. Mix the artichokes, Parmesan, and 1 tbsp of the thyme in a small bowl.
2. Cut a 2-inch pocket in the thickest part of each chicken breast. Stuff a quarter of the artichoke mixture into each pocket.
3. Rub the chicken breasts with 1 tsp of the oil and season with ¾ tsp salt and ¼ tsp pepper.
4. Heat grill or grill pan to medium. Grill the chicken, turning once, until cooked through, 6 to 7 minutes per side.
5. Mix the tomatoes, shallot, vinegar, ¼ tsp each salt and pepper, and the remaining oil and thyme in a large bowl.
6. Slice the chicken, if desired, and serve with the tomato salad and baguette slices, if using.

Nutrition:

Calories: 413 kcal

Protein: 24.07g

Fat: 14.24g

Saturated Fat: 3.4g

Cholesterol: 40mg

18.Feta Chicken with Zucchini

Preparation Time: 20 Minutes

Cooking Time: 15 Minutes

Servings: 4

Ingredients

- 2 tbsp olive oil
- 1 lemon
- 4 boneless, skinless chicken breasts (about 1 1/2 pounds)
- ¼ tsp kosher salt
- 2 medium zucchini
- ¼ cup fresh flat-leaf parsley leaves, chopped
- .13 tsp black pepper
- 1/3 cup (about 2 ounces) crumbled Feta

Directions

1. Heat oven to 400° F. Drizzle ½ tbsp of the oil in a roasting pan. Remove the zest from the lemon in thin strips; set aside. Thinly slice the lemon. Place half the slices in the pan.
2. Place the chicken on top of the lemon slices and season with 1/8 tsp of the salt.
3. Slice each zucchini in half lengthwise, then slice each half into ¼-inch-thick half-moons. In a bowl, combine the zucchini, parsley, and pepper and the remaining oil, lemon slices, and salt; toss.
4. Spread the mixture around the chicken and sprinkle the Feta over the top.
5. Roast until the chicken is cooked through, 15 to 20 minutes. Transfer it to a cutting board and cut each piece into thirds.
6. Divide the chicken, zucchini mixture, and lemons among individual plates and sprinkle with the zest.

Nutrition:

Calories: 270 kcal

Calories from fat: 27%

Fat: 8g

Saturated fat: 3g

Cholesterol: 110mg

Sodium: 378mg

Carbohydrates: 5g

Fiber: 2g

Sugars: 3g

Protein: 42g

19.Cinnamon Chicken

Preparation Time: 10 Minutes

Cooking Time: 30 Minutes

Servings: 4

Ingredients

- 4 skinless, boneless chicken breast halves
- 1 tsp ground cinnamon
- 2 tbsp Italian-style seasoning
- 1 1/2 tsp garlic powder
- 3 tsp salt
- 1 tsp ground black pepper

Direction:

1. Preheat oven to 350 degrees F (175 degrees C).
2. Place chicken in a lightly greased 9x13 inch baking dish. Sprinkle evenly with ground cinnamon, seasoning, garlic powder, salt and pepper. (Note: You can be liberal with the seasoning, garlic powder, salt and pepper; however, the cinnamon should only be a dusting and not clumped.)
3. Bake at 350 degrees F (175 degrees C) for about 30 minutes or until chicken is cooked through and juices run clear.

Nutrition:

Calories: 143 kcal

Protein: 27.7g

Carbohydrates: 3g

Fat: 1.7g

Cholesterol: 68.4mg

Sodium: 1821.7mg

20.Chinese Five Spice Chicken

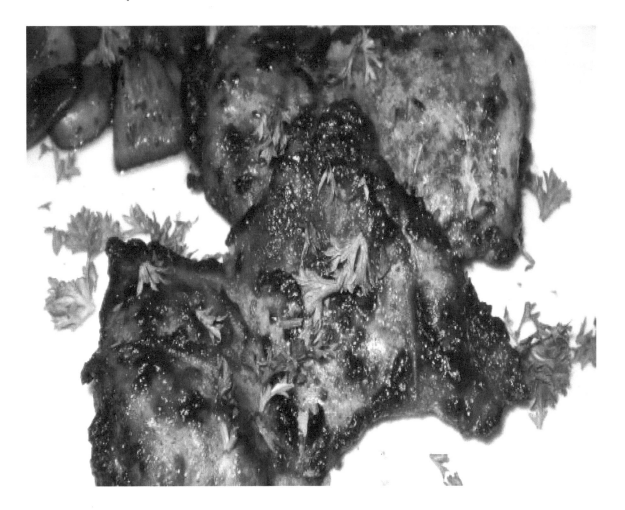

Preparation Time: 1 hour 15 Minutes

Cooking Time: 30 Minutes

Servings: 4-6

Ingredients

- 1 kg chicken piece
- 1 medium onion, finely chopped
- 1 -3 cloves of garlic, finely chopped
- 1/3 cup soy sauce
- 2 tbsp peanut oil
- 2 tsp five-spice powder

Direction:

1. Place the chicken pieces in a large dish or plastic bag.
2. Mix the remaining ingredients and pour over the chicken.
3. Marinate refrigerated overnight or for 1 to 2 hours if time is short.
4. Transfer the chicken to a baking dish and brush with the marinade.
5. Cook uncovered in a preheated 350F (180C) oven, brushing once or twice with the marinade until the chicken is done, about one hour.

Nutrition:

Calories: 331 kcal

Protein: 38.24g

Carbohydrates: 12.61g

Fat: 13.22g

Cholesterol: 112mg

Sodium: 787mg

21.Chicken with Acorn Squash and Tomatoes

Preparation Time: 20 Minutes

Cooking Time: 10 Minutes

Servings: 4

Ingredients

- 1 small acorn squash (about 1 1/2 pounds), halved, seeded, and sliced 1/4 inch thick
- 1-pint grape tomatoes, halved
- 4 cloves of garlic, sliced
- 3 tbsp olive oil

- kosher salt and black pepper
- 4-6-ounce boneless, skinless chicken breasts
- ½ tsp ground coriander
- 2 tbsp chopped fresh oregano

Direction:

1. Heat oven to 425° F.
2. On a large rimmed baking sheet, toss the squash, tomatoes and garlic with 2 tablespoons of the oil, ½ tsp salt and ¼ tsp pepper.
3. Roast the vegetables until the squash is tender, 20 to 25 minutes.
4. Meanwhile, heat the remaining tablespoon of oil in a large skillet over medium heat.
5. Season the chicken with the coriander, ½ tsp salt and ¼ tsp pepper. Cook until golden brown and cooked through, 6 to 7 minutes per side.
6. Serve the chicken with the squash and tomatoes and sprinkle with the oregano.

Nutrition:

Calories: 361 kcal

Fat: 15g

Saturated fat: 3g

Cholesterol: 94mg

Sodium: 572mg

Protein: 37g

Carbohydrates: 22g

Sugars: 6g

Fiber: 4g

Iron: 3mg

Calcium: 96mg.

22.Chicken Cordon Bleu

Preparation Time: 10 Minutes

Cooking Time: 35 Minutes

Servings: 4

Ingredients

- 4 skinless, boneless chicken breast halves
- ¼ tsp salt
- 1/8 tsp ground black pepper
- 6 slices Swiss cheese
- 4 slices cooked ham

- ½ cup seasoned bread crumbs

Direction

1. Preheat oven to 350 degrees F (175 degrees C). Coat a 7x11 inch baking dish with nonstick cooking spray.
2. Pound chicken breasts to 1/4-inch thickness.
3. Sprinkle each piece of chicken on both sides with salt and pepper. Place 1 cheese slice and 1 ham slice on top of each breast. Roll up each breast, and secure them with a toothpick. Place in a baking dish, and sprinkle chicken evenly with bread crumbs.
4. Bake for 30 to 35 minutes, or until chicken is no longer pink. Remove from oven, and place 1/2 cheese slice on top of each breast. Return to oven for 3 to 5 minutes, or until cheese has melted. Remove toothpicks, and serve immediately.

Nutrition:

Calories: 195 kcal

Protein: 15.61g

Carbohydrates: 4.78g

Fat: 13.22g

Cholesterol: 48mg

Sodium: 490mg

Chapter 10.   **Pork Recipes**

23.Brown Sugar Italian Pork

Preparation Time: 15 minutes

Cooking Time: 6 minutes

Servings: 6

Ingredients:

- 6 boneless pork chops
- ¾ cup white wine
- ½ cup brown sugar
- 3 tbsp Italian seasoning
- 1 tbsp olive oil

Directions:

1. Heat olive oil in your cooker with the lid off, on the "chicken/meat" setting.
2. While that heats up, season pork generously with Italian seasoning and brown sugar.
3. Add pork to the cooker and sear on both sides till golden.
4. Pour in white wine and seal the lid.
5. Adjust cook time to 6 minutes.
6. When time is up, hit "cancel" and quick-release.
7. Make sure pork has reached 145-degrees F.
8. Rest for 5 minutes before serving!

Nutrition:

Total calories: 315 kcal

Protein: 23g

Carbs: 27g

Fat: 13g

Fiber: 0g

24. Apricot-Glazed Pork Chops

Preparation Time: 15 minutes

Cooking Time: 6 minutes

Servings: 6

Ingredients:

- 6 boneless pork chops
- ½ cup apricot preserving:
- 1 tbsp balsamic vinegar
- 2 tsp olive oil
- Black pepper to taste

Directions:

1. Add oil to your cooker and heat on "chicken/meat," leaving the lid off.
2. Sprinkle black pepper on the pork chops.
3. Sear chops in the cooker on both sides till golden.
4. Mix balsamic and apricot preserving: together.
5. Pour over the pork and seal the cooker lid.
6. Adjust cook time to 6 minutes.
7. When time is up, hit "cancel" and quick-release.
8. Test temperature of pork— it should be 145-degrees F.
9. Rest for 5 minutes before serving!

Nutrition:

Total calories: 296 kcal

Protein: 20g

Carbs: 18g

Fat: 16g

Fiber: 0g

25.Easy Pork Ribs

Preparation Time: 10 minutes

Cooking Time: 15 minutes

Servings: 6

Ingredients:

- 3 pounds boneless pork ribs
- ½ cup soy sauce
- ¼ cup ketchup
- 2 tbsp olive oil
- Black pepper to taste

Directions:

1. Pour oil into your PPCXL and hit "chicken/meat," leaving the lid off.
2. When the oil is hot, add ribs and sear till golden on both sides.
3. In a bowl, mix black pepper, soy sauce and ketchup.
4. Pour over ribs and seal the lid.
5. Adjust cook time to 15 minutes.
6. When the timer beeps, hit "cancel" and wait 5 minutes before quick-releasing.
7. Make sure pork is at least 145-degrees before serving.

Nutrition:

Total calories: 570 kcal

Protein: 65g

Carbs: 0g

Fat: 27g

Fiber: 0g

26.Pineapple-BBQ Pork

Preparation Time: 10 minutes

Cooking Time: 6 minutes

Servings: 4

Ingredients:

- 4 bone-in pork loin chops
- 1 8-ounce can of undrained crushed pineapple
- 1 cup honey BBQ sauce
- 2 tbsp chili sauce
- 1 tbsp olive oil

Directions:

1. Mix can of pineapple, BBQ sauce, and chili sauce.
2. Turn your PPCXL to "chicken/meat" and heat.
3. When hot, add olive oil.
4. When the oil is sizzling, sear pork chops on both sides, 3-4 minutes per side.
5. When brown, pour sauce over the pork and seal the lid.
6. Adjust time to 6 minutes.
7. When time is up, hit "cancel" and wait 5 minutes before quick-releasing.
8. Pork should be cooked to 145-degrees.
9. Serve with sauce.

Nutrition:

Total calories: 370 kcal

Protein: 28g

Carbs: 37g

Fat: 13g

Fiber: 0g

27.Apple-Garlic Pork Loin

Preparation Time: 5 minutes

Cooking Time: 25 minutes

Servings: 12

Ingredients:

- 1– 3-pound boneless pork loin roast
- 1– 12-ounce jar of apple jelly
- 1/3 cup water
- 1 tbsp Herbes de Provence
- 2 tsp minced garlic

Directions:

1. Put pork loin in your cooker. Cut in half if necessary.
2. Mix garlic, water, and jelly.
3. Pour over pork.
4. Season with Herbes de Provence.
5. Seal the lid.
6. Hit "chicken/meat" and adjust the time to 25 minutes.
7. When time is up, hit "cancel" and wait 10 minutes before quick-releasing.
8. Pork should be served at 145-degrees. If not cooked through yet, hit "chicken/meat" and cook with the lid off until the temperature is reached.
9. Rest for 15 minutes before slicing.

Nutrition:

Total calories: 236 kcal

Protein: 26g

Carbs: 19g

Fat: 6g

Fiber: 0g

28.Garden Herb New York Strip Steaks

Preparation Time: 40 minutes

Cooking Time: 40 minutes

Servings: 4

Ingredients:

- 2 beef Strip Steaks Boneless, cut 1 inch thick (about 10 ounces each)
- Salt

Seasoning:

- 2 tbsp chopped fresh thyme
- 1 tbsp chopped fresh oregano
- 2 tsp freshly grated lemon peel

- 3 cloves of garlic, chopped
- ¼ tsp pepper

Direction:

1. Combine Seasoning ingredients in a small bowl; reserve 2 tsp for garnish. Press remaining seasoning evenly onto beef steaks.
2. Place steaks on grid over medium, ash-covered coals. Grill, covered, 11 to 14 minutes (over medium heat on a preheated gas grill, 11 to 15 minutes) for medium rare (145°F) to medium (160°F) doneness, turning occasionally.
3. Carve steaks into slices. Sprinkle with reserved seasoning and salt, as desired.
4. Beef. It's What's For Dinner

Nutrition:

Total calories: 197 kcal

Protein: 23.4g

Carbs: 19g

Fat: 10.3g

Fiber: 0.4g

29. Orange Pork and Broccoli Stir-Fry

Preparation Time: 0 minutes

Cooking Time: 10 minutes

Servings: 4

Ingredients:

- 2 pork tenderloins (1 1/2 to 2 pounds total), 4 skinless, boneless chicken-breast halves, or 1 1/2 pounds skinless salmon fillet; meat or fish cut into bite-size pieces
- 2 tbsp sherry or white wine
- ½ tsp crushed red pepper flakes
- 4 tsp cornstarch

- 1 orange, zest grated and juice squeezed
- ½ cup chicken broth
- 2 tbsp soy sauce
- 2 tsp sugar
- 2 tbsp canola oil
- 1 onion, cut into thin wedges
- ½ bunch broccoli (1/2 pound), cut into small pieces, stalks peeled and thinly sliced (3 cups)

Directions

1. In a bowl, toss the meat or fish with the sherry, red pepper, and 2 tsp of cornstarch. In a measuring cup, combine the orange juice, chicken broth, soy sauce, sugar, and the remaining cornstarch.
2. In a large nonstick skillet or wok, heat the oil over medium-high heat. Add the orange zest and let it sizzle for 1 minute. Add the onion and the meat or fish and cook, stirring, until cooked through, 2 to 5 minutes. Add the orange-juice mixture and broccoli. Simmer for 5 minutes or until the broccoli is tender.

Nutrition:

Total calories: 501 kcal

Protein: 67.22g

Carbs: 12.76g

Fat: 18.56g

Fiber: 1g

Chapter 11. **Soup Recipes**

30. Chicken Enchilada Soup

Preparation Time: 10 minutes

Cooking Time: 45 minutes

Servings: 4

Ingredients:

- ½ c. fresh cilantro, chopped
- 1 ¼ tsp. chili powder
- 1 c. fresh tomatoes, diced
- 1 med. yellow onion, diced
- 1 sm. red bell pepper, diced
- 1 tbsp. cumin, ground
- 1 tbsp. extra virgin olive oil
- 1 tbsp. lime juice, fresh
- 1 tsp. dried oregano
- 2 cloves of garlic, minced
- 2 lg. celery stalks, diced
- 4 c. chicken broth
- 8 oz. chicken thighs, boneless and skinless, shredded
- 8 oz. cream cheese, softened

Direction:

1. In a pot over medium heat, warm olive oil.
2. Once hot, add celery, red pepper, onion, and garlic. Cook for about 3 minutes or until shiny.
3. Stir the tomatoes into the pot and let cook for another 2 minutes.
4. Add seasonings to the pot, stir in chicken broth and bring to a boil.
5. Once boiling, drop the heat down to low and allow to simmer for 20 minutes.
6. Once simmering, add the cream cheese and allow the soup to return to a boil.
7. Drop the heat once again and allow to simmer for another 20 minutes.

8. Stir the shredded chicken into the soup along with the lime juice and the cilantro.

9. Spoon into bowls and serve hot!

Nutrition:

Calories: 420 kcal

Carbohydrates: 9g

Fat: 29.5g

Protein: 27g

31.Buffalo Chicken Soup

Preparation Time: 20 minutes

Cooking Time: 20 minutes

Servings: 4

Ingredients:

- 1 tablespoon olive oil
- 1 tablespoon butter
- 1/2 medium onion chopped
- 2 sticks celery chopped small
- 2 medium carrots peeled & chopped small
- 1 tablespoon flour
- 1 (1 ounce) packet ranch seasoning (I used Hidden Valley)
- 4 cups chicken broth
- 1/4 cup Frank's Red-Hot Original Sauce
- 4 chicken breasts
- 8 ounces cream cheese (I used a block of Philly)
- Salt & pepper to taste
- Garnish (optional): crumbled blue cheese, chopped scallions

Direction:

1. Take the cream cheese out of the fridge and let it soften up prior to starting the recipe or microwave it for 20-30 seconds.
2. Add the oil + butter to a pot over medium-high heat. Sauté the onion, celery, and carrot for about 7 minutes.
3. Stir in the flour and ranch seasoning, followed by the chicken broth and Frank's Red Hot.
4. Add the chicken breasts (no need to cut them up) to the pot. Increase the heat to high and bring the soup to a boil. Once it's boiling, reduce the heat so the soup is simmering. Let it cook for 12 minutes.
5. Take the chicken out of the pan and place it on a cutting board. Meanwhile, add the cream cheese to the soup. Cut up the chicken. It should be mostly cooked, but if it's not quite done yet, that's fine. You may need to give the cream cheese a helping hand with your spoon. Add the cut-up chicken into the soup once the cream cheese is incorporated.

6. If the chicken wasn't quite cooked, let it cook for a few more minutes. Season the soup with salt & pepper as needed. Serve and garnish as desired. If you love blue cheese, you can stir some right into the soup prior to dishing it up.

Nutrition:

Calories: 363 kcal

Carbohydrates: 4g

Fat: 32.5g

Protein: 57g

32. Slow Cooker Taco Soup

Preparation Time: 10 minutes

Cooking Time: 2 hours

Servings: 8

Ingredients:

- ¼ c. sour cream
- ½ c. cheddar cheese, shredded
- 2 c. diced tomatoes
- 2 lbs. ground beef
- 3 tbsp. taco seasoning*
- 4 c. chicken broth
- 8 oz. cream cheese, cubed**

Direction:

1. Heat a medium saucepan over medium heat and brown the beef.
2. Drain the fat from the beef and then place it into the slow cooker.
3. Add the cream cheese cubes, taco seasoning, and diced tomatoes into the slow cooker.
4. Add the chicken broth, cover, and leave to cook on high for two hours.
5. Once the time is up, stir all the ingredients and spoon the soup into bowls.
6. Serve hot with sour cream and shredded cheese on top!
7. *Check the label! Make sure that the taco seasoning you buy doesn't contain hidden sugars or starches.
8. **Cream cheese is easier to cut when it's very cold, and if you carefully spread a little bit of olive oil on the blade of the knife!

Nutrition:

Calories: 305 kcal

Carbohydrates: 8.5g

Fat: 31.5g

Protein: 43.5g

33.Wedding Soup

Preparation Time: 5 minutes

Cooking Time: 10 minutes

Servings: 4

Ingredients:

- ½ c. almond flour
- ½ c. parmesan cheese, grated
- ½ sm. yellow onion, diced
- 1 lb. ground beef
- 1 lg. egg, beaten
- 1 tsp. Italian seasoning
- 1 tsp. oregano, fresh & chopped
- 1 tsp. thyme, fresh & chopped
- 2 c. baby leaf spinach, fresh
- 2 c. cauliflower, riced
- 2 med. stalks celery, diced
- 2 tbsp. extra virgin olive oil
- 3 cloves of garlic, minced
- 6 c. chicken broth
- Sea salt and pepper to taste

Direction:

1. In a large mixing bowl, combine almond flour, parmesan cheese, ground beef, egg, salt, pepper, and Italian seasoning. Mix thoroughly by hand
2. Shape the meat mixture into one-inch meatballs, cover, and refrigerate until ready to cook.
3. In a large saucepan over medium heat, warm the olive oil.
4. Once the oil is hot, stir the celery and onion into the pan and season to taste with salt and pepper.
5. Stirring often, bring the onion and celery to a lightly cooked state, about six or seven minutes.
6. Add the garlic to the pan, stir to combine, and allow to cook for one more minute.
7. Stir chicken broth, fresh oregano, and the fresh thyme into the pan and stir to combine.
8. Bring the mixture to a boil.

9. Drop the heat to low and allow to simmer for about ten minutes before adding cauliflower and meatballs to it.

10. Allow cooking for about five minutes, or until the meatballs are cooked all the way through.

11. Add the spinach to the soup and stir in for about one to two minutes, or until it's sufficiently wilted.

12. Add seasoning as is needed.

13. Serve hot!

Nutrition:

Calories: 320 kcal

Carbohydrates: 4g

Fat: 26g

Protein: 6.5g

34.Teriyaki Sauce

Preparation Time: 10 minutes

Cooking Time: 30 minutes

Servings: 1

Ingredients

- 7 fl oz soy sauce
- 7 fl oz pineapple juice
- 1 tsp red wine vinegar
- 1-inch chunk of fresh ginger root, peeled and chopped
- 2 cloves of garlic

Directions

1. Place the ingredients into a saucepan, bring them to boil, reduce the heat and simmer for 10 minutes.
2. Let it cool, then remove the garlic and ginger.
3. Store it in a container in the fridge until ready to use. Use as a marinade for meat, fish, and tofu dishes.

Nutrition:

Calories: 267 kcal

Sodium: 33mg

Dietary Fiber: 1.2g

Total Fat: 4.3g

Total Carbs: 16.2g

Protein: 1.3g

35.Turmeric & Lemon Dressing

Preparation Time: 10 minutes

Cooking Time: 0 minutes

Servings: 1

Ingredients

- 1 tsp turmeric
- 4 tbsp olive oil
- Juice of 1 lemon

Directions

1. Combine all the ingredients in a bowl and serve with salads. Eat straight away.

Nutrition:

Calories: 125 kcal

Sodium: 32 mg

Dietary Fiber: 1.6g

Total Fat: 3.3g

Total Carbs: 16.3g

Protein: 1.5g

36.Garlic Vinaigrette

Preparation Time: 10 minutes

Cooking Time: 30 minutes

Servings: 1

Ingredients

- 1 clove of garlic, crushed
- 4 tbsp olive oil
- 1 tbsp lemon juice
- Freshly ground black pepper

Directions

1. Simply mix all of the ingredients together. It can either be stored or used straight away.

Nutrition:

Calories: 104 kcal

Sodium: 35 mg

Dietary Fiber: 1.3g

Total Fat: 3.1g

Total Carbs: 16.2g

Protein: 1.3g

37.Thai Salsa

Preparation Time: 20 minutes

Cooking Time: 40 minutes

Servings: 1

Ingredients

- 1 small tomato
- Chicken breast
- Turmeric
- Buckwheat
- 1 Thai chili, thinly sliced
- 1 tsp of caper
- Parsley, 2 tsp finely cut
- 1/4 of a lemon juice

Directions

1. Remove the tomato seeds to make the salsa and slice it finely, ensuring that the fluid remains in as much as possible. Combine chile, capers, lemon juice and parsley. You might mix the seeds as well, but the end product is a little different.
2. Oven to 220 degrees Celsius (425 ° F), in one tsp, marinate the chicken breast with a little oil and lemon juice. Leave for 5 to 10 minutes.
3. Then add the marinated chicken and cook on either side for about a minute, until pale golden, transfer to the oven (on a baking tray, if your pan is not ovenproof), 8 to 10 minutes or until cooked. Remove from the oven, cover with foil, and wait five minutes before eating.
4. Cook the kale for 5 minutes in a steamer in the meantime, add a little butter, fry the red onions and the ginger and then mix in the fluffy but not browned mix.
5. Cook the buckwheat with the remaining tsp of turmeric according to the package instructions. Eat rice, tomatoes, and salsa. Eat together.

Nutrition:

Calories: 104 kcal

Sodium: 33mg

Dietary Fiber: 1.6g

Total Fat: 4.3g

Total Carbs: 15.3g

Protein: 1.3g

38.Walnut Vinaigrette

Preparation Time: 10 minutes

Cooking Time: 10 minutes

Servings: 1

Ingredients

- 1 clove of garlic, finely chopped
- 6 tbsp olive oil
- 3 tbsp red wine vinegar
- 1 tbsp walnut oil
- Sea salt
- Freshly ground black pepper

Directions

1. Combine all of the ingredients in a bowl or container and season with salt and pepper. Use immediately or store in the fridge.

Nutrition:

Calories: 109 kcal

Sodium: 33 mg

Dietary Fiber: 1.6g

Total Fat: 4.3g

Total Carbs: 16.4g

Protein: 1.6g

39.Walnut & Mint Pesto

Preparation Time: 10 minutes

Cooking Time: 10 minutes

Servings: 1

Ingredients

- 6 tbsp fresh mint leaves
- 2oz walnuts
- 2 cloves of garlic
- 3½oz Parmesan cheese
- 1 tbsp lemon juice

Direction

1. Put all the ingredients into a food processor and blend until it becomes a smooth paste.

Nutrition:

Calories: 99 kcal

Sodium: 33 mg

Dietary Fiber: 1.6g

Total Fat: 4.4g

Total Carbs: 16.4g

Protein: 1.6g

40.Black Bean soup

Preparation Time: 15 minutes

Cooking Time: 20 minutes

Servings: 4

Ingredients:

- 2 tbsp. extra-virgin olive oil
- 1 medium red onion, finely chopped
- 2 cloves of garlic, minced
- 1 tbsp. minced jalapeños

- 1 tbsp. tomato paste
- kosher salt
- Freshly ground black pepper
- 1 tsp. chili powder
- 1/2 tsp. cumin
- 3 (15-oz.) cans black beans, with liquid
- 1 qt. low-sodium chicken or vegetable stock
- 1 bay leaf
- sour cream, for garnish
- Sliced avocado, for garnish
- Chopped fresh cilantro, for garnish

Direction:

2. In a large pot over medium heat, heat oil. Add onion and cook until soft and translucent, about 5 minutes. Add jalapeños and garlic and cook until fragrant, about 2 minutes. Add tomato paste, stir to coat vegetables, and cook about a minute more. Season with salt, pepper, chili powder, and cumin and stir to coat.

3. Add black beans with their liquid and chicken broth. Stir soup, add bay leaf and bring to a boil. Immediately reduce to a simmer and let simmer until slightly reduced about 15 minutes. Remove bay leaf.

4. Using an immersion blender or food processor, blend the soup to the desired consistency.

5. Serve with a dollop of sour cream, sliced avocado and cilantro.

Nutrition:

Calories: 174 kcal

Sodium: 91mg

Dietary Fiber: 8.4g

Total Fat: 11.57g

Total Carbs: 17.86g

Protein: 4.15g

41.Cold Tomato Summer Vegetable Soup

Preparation Time: 15 minutes

Cooking Time: 20 minutes

Servings: 4

Ingredients:

- 6 fresh, ripe tomatoes, seeds removed (cut tomatoes in half, squeeze out seeds into a sieve over a bowl to catch the juice, use the juice, discard the seeds), chopped
- 1 cucumber, peeled, seeded, chopped fine
- 1 red bell pepper, chopped fine
- 2 stalks celery, chopped fine
- 1 tbsp fresh dill, chopped
- 2 cloves of garlic, minced
- 2 tsp sugar
- 2 zucchini, chopped fine
- 1/2 medium sweet onion, chopped fine
- 1-2 tsp salt
- 1/2 tsp freshly ground black pepper
- 3 cups tomato juice (in addition to the juice made when you squeezed the tomatoes above)
- 1 tsp Worcestershire sauce
- 2 tbsp extra virgin olive oil
- 1/4 cup sherry vinegar
- 1 tsp chopped fresh oregano (or a pinch of dry)
- 1 1/2 cups vegetable broth
- Hot sauce if needed

Direction:

1. Combine all ingredients in a large bowl. Use the additional tomato juice to thin the soup to the desired consistency. Adjust seasonings to taste. Better the next day.

Nutrition:

Calories: 842 kcal

Sodium: 91mg

Dietary Fiber: 86.03g

Total Fat: 11.57g

Total Carbs: 23.94g

Protein: 4.69g

Chapter 12.   **Dessert Recipes**

42. Yogurt Mint

Preparation Time: 5 minutes

Cooking Time: 10 minutes

Servings: 2

Ingredients:

- 1 cup of water
- 5 cups of milk
- ¾ cup plain yogurt
- ¼ cup fresh mint
- 1 tbsp. maple syrup

Directions:

2. Add 1 cup water to the Instant Pot Pressure Cooker.
3. Press the STEAM function button and adjust to 1 minute.
4. Once done, add the milk, then press the YOGURT function button and allow boiling.
5. Add yogurt and fresh mint, then stir well.
6. Pour into a glass and add maple syrup.
7. Enjoy.

Nutrition:

Calories: 25 kcal

Fat: 0.5g

Carbs: 5g

Protein: 2g

43.Chocolate Fondue

Preparation Time: 5 minutes

Cooking Time: 10 minutes

Servings: 2

Ingredients:

- 1 cup water
- ½ tsp. sugar
- ½ cup coconut cream
- ¾ cup dark chocolate, chopped

Directions:

1. Pour the water into your Instant Pot.
2. To a heatproof bowl, add the chocolate, sugar, and coconut cream.
3. Place in the Instant Pot.
4. Seal the lid, select MANUAL, and cook for 2 minutes. When ready, do a quick release and carefully open the lid. Stir well and serve immediately.

Nutrition:

Calories: 216 kcal

Fat: 17g

Carbs: 11g

Protein: 2g

44.Rice Pudding

Preparation Time: 5 minutes

Cooking Time: 12 minutes

Servings: 2

Ingredients:

- ½ cup short grain rice
- ¼ cup of sugar
- 1 cinnamon stick
- 1½ cup milk
- 1 slice lemon peel
- Salt to taste

Directions:

1. Rinse the rice under cold water.
2. Put the milk, cinnamon stick, sugar, salt, and lemon peel inside the Instant Pot Pressure Cooker.
3. Close the lid, lock it in place and make sure to seal the valve. Press the PRESSURE button and cook for 10 minutes on HIGH.
4. When the timer beeps, choose the QUICK PRESSURE release. This will take about 2 minutes.
5. Remove the lid. Open the pressure cooker and discard the lemon peel and cinnamon stick. Spoon in a serving bowl and serve.

Nutrition:

Calories: 111 kcal

Fat: 6g

Carbs: 21g

Protein: 3g

45.Braised Apples

Preparation Time: 5 minutes

Cooking Time: 12 minutes

Servings: 2

Ingredients:

- 2 cored apples
- ½ cup of water
- ½ cup red wine
- 3 tbsp. sugar
- ½ tsp. ground cinnamon

Directions:

1. In the bottom of Instant Pot, add the water and place apples.
2. Pour wine on top and sprinkle with sugar and cinnamon. Close the lid carefully and cook for 10 minutes at HIGH PRESSURE.
3. When done, do a quick pressure release.
4. Transfer the apples onto serving plates and top with cooking liquid.
5. Serve immediately.

Nutrition:

Calories: 245 kcal

Fat: 0.5g

Carbs: 53g

Protein: 1g

46. Wine Figs

Preparation Time: 5 minutes

Cooking Time: 3 minutes

Servings: 2

Ingredients:

- ½ cup pine nuts
- 1 cup red wine
- 1 lb. figs
- Sugar, as needed

Directions:

1. Slowly pour the wine and sugar into the Instant Pot.
2. Arrange the trivet inside it; place the figs over it. Close the lid and lock. Ensure that you have sealed the valve to avoid leakage.
3. Press MANUAL mode and set a timer to 3 minutes.
4. After the timer reads zero, press CANCEL and quick-release pressure.
5. Carefully remove the lid.
6. Divide figs into bowls, and drizzle wine from the pot over them.
7. Top with pine nuts and enjoy.

Nutrition:

Calories: 95 kcal

Fat: 3g

Carbs: 5g

Protein: 2g

47.Mint Chocolate Cheesecake Cupcakes

Preparation Time: 25 minutes

Cooking Time: 35 minutes

Servings: 12

Ingredients:

- 1 1/2 cups all-purpose flour
- 1 teaspoon baking soda
- 1/2 teaspoon salt
- 1/4 cup cocoa powder
- 1 cup granulated sugar
- 1 tablespoon white vinegar
- 1 teaspoon pure vanilla extract
- 1/3 cup oil
- 1 cup cold water

- 4 oz. softened cream cheese
- 1 egg yolk
- 1 cup chopped Andes chocolate mints (25 mints)

Direction:

1. Preheat the oven to 350°F and line a 12-count muffin tin with cupcake liners.
2. In a large bowl, whisk together the flour, baking soda, salt, cocoa powder and sugar. Make 3 wells in the dry ingredients: 1 small, 1 medium, and 1 large. Measure the vanilla into the small well, the vinegar into the medium, and the oil into the large. Pour the cold water over top and whisk until the batter is smooth.
3. Add the softened cream cheese and egg yolk to a small bowl and whip using a handheld electric mixer on medium speed until smooth and creamy. Fold in the chocolate mint pieces.
4. Fill each cupcake liner half full with the chocolate batter, then drop 1-2 teaspoons of cheesecake filling in the middle of each, finally cover with about 1 tablespoon of the remaining chocolate batter. They should be filled all the way to the top with batter and cheesecake filling.
5. Bake the cupcakes in the preheated oven for 30-35 minute or until a toothpick inserted into the cake part around the edges of the cupcake comes out clean. Let cool for 10 minutes and then remove from the muffin tin to finish cooling on a wire rack.
6. Refrigerate until ready to serve. These are great served with whipped cream on top. Enjoy! **Nutrition:**

Calories: 250 kcal

Fat: 9.74g

Carbs: 37.99g

Protein: 3.36g

Chapter 13. **Breakfast Recipes**

48.Optavia Biscuit Pizza

Preparation Time: 5 minutes

Cooking Time: 15-20 minutes

Servings: 1

Ingredients:

- 1/4 sachet of Optavia buttermilk cheddar and herb biscuit
- 1/4 tbsp of tomato sauce
- 1/4 tbsp of low-fat shredded cheese

- 1/4 tbsp of water
- Parchment paper

Directions:

1. You may begin by preheating the oven to 350°F
2. Mix the biscuit and water and stir properly.
3. In the parchment paper, pour the mixture and spread it into a thin circle. Allow cooking for 10 minutes.
4. Take it out and add the tomato sauce and shredded cheese.
5. Bake it for a few more minutes.

Nutrition:

Calories: 478 kcal

Protein: 30g

Carbohydrates: 22g

Fats: 29g

49. Lean and Green Smoothie 1

Preparation Time: 5 minutes

Cooking Time: 0 minutes

Servings: 1

Ingredients:

- 2 1/2 cups of kale leaves
- 3/4 cup of chilled apple juice
- 1 cup of cubed pineapple
- 1/2 cup of frozen green grapes
- 1/2 cup of chopped apple

Directions:

1. Place the pineapple, apple juice, apple, frozen seedless grapes, and kale leaves in a blender.

2. Cover and blend until it's smooth.

3. Smoothie is ready and can be garnished with halved grapes if you wish.

Nutrition:

Calories: 81 kcal

Protein: 2g

Carbohydrates: 19g

Fat: 1g

50.Lean and Green Smoothie 2

Preparation Time: 5 minutes

Cooking Time: 0 minutes

Servings: 1

Ingredients:

- 6 kale leaves
- 2 peeled oranges
- 2 cups of mango kombucha
- 2 cups of chopped pineapple
- 2 cups of water

Directions:

1. Break up the oranges, place in the blender,
2. Add the mango kombucha, chopped pineapple, and kale leaves into the blender,
3. Blend everything until it is smooth.
4. Smoothie is ready to be taken.

Nutrition:

Calories: 81 kcal

Protein: 2g

Carbohydrates: 19g

Fat: 1g

51.Cinnamon Crescent Rolls

Preparation Time: 5 minutes

Cooking Time: 10 minutes

Servings: 4

Ingredients:

- 1 tube (8 counts) Pillsbury Crescent Rolls, unrolled and separated

Filling

- 4 tbsp butter, softened
- ¼ cup white sugar
- 2½ tsp cinnamon

Glaze

- 2 tbsp butter, melted
- ¼ cup + 2 tbsp powdered Sugar
- ½ tsp vanilla extract

Direction:

1. Preheat oven to 375
2. Place the unrolled and separated crescent rolls on an ungreased rimmed cookie sheet (one with sides).

Filling:

1. In a small bowl, mix together the butter, sugar and cinnamon

Assemble:

1. Evenly spread the cinnamon and butter over the crescent rolls and roll up tightly.
2. Place tip side down on the cookie sheet.
3. Bake for 10-12 minutes.

Glaze:

1. In a small bowl, mix together the butter, powdered sugar and vanilla until smooth.
2. Place in a zip lock bag and snip a tiny corner off.
3. Drizzle the glaze over the cinnamon rolls.

Nutrition:

Calories: 201kcal

Protein: 0.93g

Carbohydrates: 6.66g

Fat: 19.76g

52.Mushroom Scrambled Eggs

Preparation Time: 10 minutes

Cooking Time: 10 minutes

Servings: 3

Ingredients:

- 2 eggs
- 1 cup of chopped canned mushroom
- 1/2 cup of chopped onion
- Salt and Black Pepper for taste
- Parsley for Garnish
- 2 tbsp of olive oil

Direction:

1. Add oil to the pan in medium heat. Once it is hot, add onion and stir it for few minutes or till it became light brown.
2. Add mushroom and stir it well. Adjust to low heat, and cover with a Lid. Let it cook for up to 4 to 5 minutes or until it turns dark brown.

3. While the mushroom is cooking, add the egg, salt and black pepper in a small bowl. Beat the egg.

4. Add the egg into the pan and stir it well. Once the egg is cooked, turn off the heat before serving.

Nutrition:

Calories: 187 kcal

Protein: 7.48g

Carbohydrates: 4.93g

Fat: 15.58g

53.Turkey Breakfast Sausages

Preparation Time: 10 minutes

Cooking Time: 10 minutes

Servings: 8

Ingredients:

- 2 pounds ground turkey
- 1 tbsp brown sugar
- 2 tsp kosher salt
- 1 1/2 tsp ground black pepper
- 1 1/2 tsp ground sage
- 1 1/2 tsp ground thyme
- ½ tsp dried marjoram
- ½ tsp red pepper flakes

Direction:

1. Mix turkey, brown sugar, salt, black pepper, sage, thyme, marjoram, and red pepper flakes in a bowl. Shape turkey mixture into patties.
2. Fry patties in a large skillet over medium-high heat until golden brown and no longer pink in the center, 6 to 8 minutes.

Nutrition:

Calories: 176 kcal

Protein: 22.6g

Carbohydrates: 2.3g

Fat: 8.6g

Cholesterol: 83.8mg

Sodium: 545mg

54.Blueberry Pancakes

Preparation Time: 5 minutes

Cooking Time: 8 minutes

Servings: 12

Ingredients:

- 2 cups all-purpose flour
- 2 tbsp baking powder
- 1 tsp kosher salt
- 3 tbsp light brown sugar
- 2 eggs
- 1 tsp vanilla
- 1 1/2 cups milk
- 5 tbsp butter, melted
- 2 cups fresh blueberries
- butter for frying

Direction:

1. In a large bowl whisk the flour, baking powder, salt and brown sugar together.

2. In a separate bowl whisk the eggs, vanilla and milk together.

3. Add the wet ingredients into the dry and mix until just combined. Lastly, mix in the melted butter and stir until combined, the batter will be slightly lumpy. Set the batter aside while you heat your griddle to medium-low heat. Melt a small pat of butter on the griddle and then scoop out 1/4 cup of pancake batter onto the hot griddle and top evenly with blueberries, as many or few as you prefer.

4. Cook until the edges are set and bubbles form on top of the pancake. Flip and cook until browned.

5. Serve warm.

Nutrition:

Calories: 197 kcal

Protein: 4.94g

Carbohydrates: 26.99g

Fat: 7.75g

Cholesterol: 119mg

Sodium: 264mg

55.Banana Pecan Muffins

Preparation Time: 10 minutes

Cooking Time: 20 minutes

Servings: 12

Ingredients:

- 2 cups all-purpose flour
- 1 1/2 tsp baking soda
- 1/2 tsp salt
- 4 very ripe large bananas
- 1 cup packed light brown sugar
- 3/4 cup butter, melted and cooled
- 2 large eggs
- 1 tsp pure vanilla extract
- 1/2 cup pecans, toasted and chopped

Direction:

1. Preheat the oven to 350 degrees F. Line a 12-cup regular-sized muffin tin with paper liners.
2. Cut two of the bananas into pieces and place in the bowl of a stand mixer fitted with the whisk attachment. Add the brown sugar and whip on medium-high speed for around three minutes or until pretty smooth.
3. Add the melted butter, eggs and vanilla to the banana sugar mixture, and keep whipping for another 2 - 3 minutes, until well combined.
4. Mash the remaining two bananas in a small bowl until mostly smooth, with only small chunks remaining.
5. In a medium bowl, whisk together the flour, baking soda and salt. Remove the bowl from the stand mixer and fold in the flour mixture with a rubber spatula until just combined. Fold in the mashed bananas.
6. Divide the batter evenly in the muffin cups. Sprinkle the tops with pecans and bake for about 18 to 20 minutes until a toothpick inserted in the center comes out clean.

Nutrition:

Calories: 322 kcal

Carbohydrates: 43g

Protein: 4g

Fat: 15g

Saturated Fat: 7g

Cholesterol: 57mg

Sodium: 351mg

56.Banana and Blueberry Muffins

Preparation Time: 10 minutes

Cooking Time: 20 minutes

Servings: 12

Ingredients:

- 2/3 cup milk
- ¼ cup vegetable oil
- ½ cup mashed very ripe banana (1 medium)
- 1 egg
- 2 cups Gold Medal™ all-purpose flour
- 2/3 cup sugar
- 2 ½ tsp baking powder
- ¼ tsp ground nutmeg

- 1 cup fresh or frozen (thawed and well-drained) blueberries

Direction:

1. Heat oven to 400°F. Grease bottoms only of 12 regular-size muffin cups or line with paper baking cups.
2. Beat milk, oil, banana and egg in a large bowl with a fork. Stir in remaining ingredients except for blueberries just until flour is moistened. Fold in blueberries. Divide batter evenly among muffin cups (cups will be almost full). Sprinkle with sugar if desired.
3. Bake 18 to 20 minutes or until golden brown. Immediately remove from pan.

Nutrition:

Calories: 100 kcal

Carbohydrates: 32g

Protein: 3g

Fat: 6g

Saturated Fat: 7g

Cholesterol: 20mg

Sodium: 210mg

57.Sweet Potato Hash

Preparation Time: 5 minutes

Cooking Time: 25 minutes

Servings: 4

Ingredients:

- 2 tbsp olive oil
- 3 medium sweet potatoes, skin-on and diced into equal, bite-size chunks
- 1/2 medium white onion, diced
- 2 stalks celery, diced
- 1 1/2 tsp sea salt
- 1/2 tsp ground black pepper
- 2 cloves garlic, minced
- sliced green onions, for garnish

Direction:

1. Heat oil in a large pan over medium-high heat.
2. Add the potatoes, onion and celery to the oil and sprinkle with salt and pepper. Stir to combine.
3. Cover and cook for 15-20 minutes, stirring occasionally until the potatoes are almost tender.
4. Turn the heat to high and add the garlic, stirring to combine. Cook on high for 2-5 more minutes until sweet potatoes are nicely browned.
5. Serve hot and with sliced green onions, if desired.

Nutrition:

Calories: 157 kcal

Carbohydrates: 22g

Protein: 1g

Fat: 7g

Saturated Fat: 1g

Sodium: 942mg

58.Crunchy and Chewy Granola

Preparation Time: 20 minutes

Cooking Time: 1 hour 15 minutes

Servings: 12

Ingredients:

- ¼ cup honey
- ¼ cup pure maple syrup
- 2 large egg whites (see Note)
- 1/3 cup vegetable oil plus oil for the baking sheet (optional)
- 1 tsp pure vanilla extract

- 1 tsp ground cinnamon
- 1 tsp kosher or coarse salt
- ½ tsp grated orange zest optional
- 4 cups old-fashioned oats, not quick-cooking
- 1 cup chopped unsalted nuts such as walnuts, pecans, pistachios, cashews, or almonds (optional)
- 2 cups mixed chopped dried fruit such as apricots or prunes, and/or dried cherries, blueberries, cranberries and raisins
- Nonstick cooking spray optional

Directions

1. Preheat the oven to 275°F.
2. Place the honey, maple syrup, egg whites, oil, vanilla, cinnamon, salt, and orange zest, if using, in a large bowl and mix until well blended. Set 1/2 cup of the honey mixture aside in a medium-size bowl. Add the oats and nuts, if using, to the large bowl and mix with a spoon or your hands until everything is well combined and coated.
3. Add the dried fruit to the reserved 1/2 cup of the honey mixture and stir to combine. Set the dried fruit mixture aside.
4. Spray a rimmed baking sheet with nonstick cooking spray, or coat it lightly with oil, or line it with parchment paper. Spread the oat mixture out on the prepared baking sheet in a thin, even layer. Bake the oat mixture for 30 minutes.
5. Add the dried fruit mixture to the oat mixture and stir well with a spoon mixture or spatula to combine. Spread the granola out again in an even layer. Bake the granola until the oats are golden brown and crunchy, 40 to 45 minutes, stirring it once more halfway through the baking time but leave some clumps! Let the granola cool on the baking sheet on a wire rack.

Nutrition:

Calories: 286 kcal

Carbohydrates: 36g

Protein: 7g

Fat: 14g

Saturated Fat: 6g

Sodium: 206mg

Chapter 14.   **Lunch Recipes**

59.Beef Burgers

Preparation Time: 15 minutes

Cooking Time: 12 minutes

Servings: 4

Ingredients:

For Burgers:

- 1-pound lean ground beef

- 1 cup fresh baby spinach leaves, chopped
- ½ of small yellow onion, chopped
- ¼ cup sun-dried tomatoes, chopped
- 1 egg, beaten
- ¼ cup feta cheese, crumbled
- Salt and ground black pepper, as required
- 2 tbsp olive oil

For Serving:

- 4 cups fresh spinach, torn
- 1 large tomato, sliced

Directions:

1. **For burgers**: In a large bowl, add all ingredients except for oil and mix until well blended.
2. Make 4 equal-sized patties from the mixture.
3. In a pan, heat the oil over medium-high heat and cook the patties for about 5-6 minutes per side or until desired doneness.
4. Divide the spinach and tomato slices and onto serving plates.
5. Top each plate with 1 burger and serve.

Nutrition:

Calories: 244 kcal

Fat: 19g

Carbohydrates: 4.9g

Fiber: 1.7g

Sugar: 2.5g

Protein: 15g

60.Salmon Burgers

Preparation Time: 15 minutes

Cooking Time: 16 minutes

Servings: 5

Ingredients:

- 1 ½ pounds skinless, boneless salmon
- 2 teaspoons Dijon mustard
- 2 shallots, peeled and cut into chunks
- ½ cup coarse bread crumbs
- 1 tablespoon capers, drained
- Salt and black pepper
- 2 tablespoons butter or olive oil
- Lemon wedges

137

- Tabasco sauce

Directions:

1. Cut the salmon into large chunks, and put about a quarter of it into the container of a food processor, along with the mustard. Turn the machine on, and let it run — stopping to scrape down the sides if necessary — until the mixture becomes pasty.
2. Add the shallots and the remaining salmon, and pulse the machine on and off until the fish is chopped and well combined with the puree. No piece should be larger than a 1/4 inch or so; be careful not make the mixture too fine.
3. Scrape the mixture into a bowl, and by hand, stir in the bread crumbs, capers and some salt and pepper. Shape into four burgers. (You can cover and refrigerate the burgers for a few hours at this point.)
4. Place the butter or oil in a 12-inch nonstick skillet, and turn the heat to medium-high. When the butter foam subsides or the oil is hot, cook the burgers for 2 to 3 minutes a side, turning once. Alternatively, you can grill them: Let them firm up on the first side, grilling about 4 minutes, before turning over and finishing for just another minute or two. To check for doneness, make a small cut and peek inside. Be careful not to overcook. Serve on a bed of greens or on buns or by themselves, with lemon wedges and Tabasco or any dressing you like.

Nutrition:

Calories: 186 kcal

Fat: 12.7g

Carbohydrates: 3.9g

Fiber: 0.8g

Sugar: 1.3g

Protein: 15.4g

61.Meatballs with Salad

Preparation Time: 20 minutes

Cooking Time: 15 minutes

Servings: 4

Ingredients:

For Meatballs:

- 1-pound lean ground turkey
- 1 cup frozen chopped spinach, thawed and squeezed
- ½ cup feta cheese, crumbled
- ½ tsp dried oregano
- Salt and ground black pepper, as required
- 2 tbsp olive oil

For Salad:

- 4 cups fresh baby spinach
- 1 cup cherry tomatoes, halved

Directions:

1. **For meatballs**: place all ingredients except for oil in a bowl and mix until well blended.
2. Make 12 equal-sized meatballs from the mixture.
3. In a large non-stick pan, heat the olive oil over medium heat and cook the meatballs for about 10-15 minutes or until done completely, flipping occasionally.
4. With a slotted spoon, place the meatballs onto a plate.
5. **Meanwhile, for salad**: in a large salad bowl, add all ingredients and toss to coat well.
6. Divide meatballs and salad onto serving plates and serve.

Nutrition:

Calories: 289 kcal

Fat: 19g

Carbohydrates: 4g

Fiber: 1.5g

Sugar: 2.1g

Protein: 26.4g

62. Stuffed Bell Peppers

Preparation Time: 20 minutes

Cooking Time: 40 minutes

Servings: 5

Ingredients:

- 5 large bell peppers, tops and seeds removed
- 1 tbsp olive oil
- ½ of a large onion, chopped
- ½ tsp dried oregano
- ½ tsp dried thyme
- Salt and ground black pepper, as required
- 1-pound grass-fed ground beef
- 1 large zucchini, chopped
- 3 tbsp homemade tomato paste

Directions:

1. Preheat your oven to 350 degrees F.
2. Grease a small baking dish.
3. In a large pan of boiling water, place the bell peppers and cook for about 4-5 minutes.
4. Remove from the water and place onto a paper towel, cut side down.
5. Meanwhile, in a large nonstick pan, heat the olive oil over medium heat and sauté onion for about 3-4 minutes.
6. Add the ground beef, oregano, salt and pepper and cook for about 8-10 minutes.
7. Add the zucchini and cook for about 2-3 minutes.
8. Remove from the heat and drain any juices from the beef mixture.
9. Add the tomato paste and stir to combine.
10. Arrange the bell peppers into the prepared baking dish, cut side upward.
11. Stuff the bell peppers with the beef mixture evenly.
12. Bake for approximately 15 minutes.
13. Serve warm.

Nutrition:

Calories: 241 kcal

Fat: 8.8g

Carbohydrates: 11g

Fiber: 3.5g

Sugar: 5.8g

Protein: 29.9g

63.Shrimp with Spinach

Preparation Time: 15 minutes

Cooking Time: 10 minutes

Servings: 4

Ingredients:

- 1 ½ cups fresh baby spinach
- 1 ½ teaspoons granulated garlic powder
- 20 frozen shrimp, thawed
- 1 teaspoon ground black pepper
- 1 tablespoon olive oil, or as needed

Directions:

1. Place spinach in a large bowl; sprinkle with garlic powder and toss. Place shrimp in a bowl; sprinkle with black pepper and toss.

2. Heat oil in a skillet over medium-high heat. Add shrimp; cook and stir until bright pink on the outside and the meat is opaque, about 5 minutes. Add spinach, cook and stir until just wilted, about 1 minute.

Nutrition:

Calories: 240 kcal

Fat: 12.3g

Carbohydrates: 7.7g

Fiber: 3.1g

Sugar: 1.7g

Protein: 28.2g

64.Scallops with Broccoli

Preparation Time: 15 minutes

Cooking Time: 9 minutes

Servings: 2

Ingredients:

- 1 tbsp olive oil
- 1 cup broccoli, cut into small pieces
- 1cloves of garlic, crushed
- ½ pound scallops
- 1 tsp fresh lemon juice
- Salt, as required

Directions:

1. In a large non-stick pan, heat oil over medium heat and cook the broccoli and garlic for about 3-4 minutes, stirring occasionally.
2. Add in the scallops and cook for about 3-4 minutes, flipping occasionally.
3. Stir in the lemon juice and salt and remove from the heat.
4. Serve hot.

Nutrition:

Calories: 178 kcal

Fat: 8g

Carbohydrates: 6.3g

Fiber: 1.2g

Sugar: 0.8g

Protein: 20.4g

65.Kale and Red Onion Dhal with Buckwheat

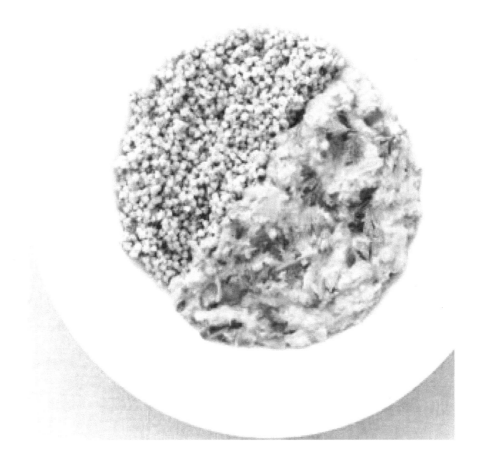

Preparation Time: 5 minutes

Cooking Time: 25 minutes

Servings: 4

Ingredients:

- 1 tbsp olive oil
- 1 small red onion, sliced
- 3 cloves of garlic, grated or crushed
- 2 cm ginger, grated
- 1 bird eye chilli, deseeded and finely chopped (more if you like things hot!)
- 2 tsp turmeric
- 2 tsp garam masala
- 160g red lentils

- 400 ml tin coconut milk
- 200 ml water (i.e. half the coconut milk can)
- 100g kale (or spinach would be a great alternative)
- 160g buckwheat (or brown rice)

Direction:

1. Put the olive oil in a large, deep saucepan and add the sliced onion. Cook on low heat, with the lid on for 5 minutes until softened.
2. Add the garlic, ginger and chilli and cook for 1 more minute.
3. Add the turmeric, garam masala and a splash of water and cook for 1 more minute.
4. Add the red lentils, coconut milk, and 200ml water (do this simply by half filling the coconut milk can with water and tipping it into the saucepan).
5. Mix everything together thoroughly and cook for 20 minutes over a gentle heat with the lid on. Stir occasionally and add a little more water if the dhal starts to stick.
6. After 20 minutes add the kale, stir thoroughly and replace the lid, cook for a further 5 minutes (1-2 minutes if you use spinach instead!)
7. About 15 minutes before the curry is ready, place the buckwheat in a medium saucepan and add plenty of boiling water. Bring the water back to the boil and cook for 10 minutes (or a little longer if you prefer your buckwheat softer. Drain the buckwheat in a sieve and serve with the dhal.

Nutrition:

Calories: 402 kcal

Fat: 7g

Carbohydrates: 71g

Fiber: 18g

Sugar: 7g

Protein: 18g

66.Lamb, Butternut Squash and Date Tagine

Preparation Time: 15 minutes

Cooking Time: 1 hour 15 minutes

Servings: 6

Ingredients:

- 2 tbsp olive oil
- 1 red onion, sliced
- 2 cm ginger, grated
- 3 cloves of garlic, grated or crushed
- 1 tsp chilli flakes to taste
- 2 tsp cumin seeds
- 1 cinnamon stick

- 2 tsp ground turmeric
- 800g lamb neck fillet, cut into 2cm chunks
- ½ tsp salt
- 100g Medjool dates, pitted and chopped
- 400g tin chopped tomatoes plus half a can of water
- 500g butternut squash, chopped into 1cm cubes
- 400g tin chickpeas, drained
- 2 tbsp fresh coriander plus extra for garnish
- Buckwheat, couscous, flatbreads or rice to serve

Direction:

1. Preheat your oven to 160C / 140C fan / gas mark 3 / 325F.

2. Drizzle 2 tbsp of olive oil into a large ovenproof saucepan or cast iron casserole dish. Add the sliced onion and cook on a gentle heat, with the lid on, for about 5 minutes, until the onions are softened but not brown.

3. Add the grated garlic and ginger, chilli, cumin, cinnamon and turmeric. Stir well and cook for 1 more minute with the lid off. Add a splash of water if it gets too dry.

4. Next, add in the lamb chunks. Stir well to coat the meat in the onions and spices and then add the salt, chopped dates and tomatoes, plus about half the tomato can of water (roughly 200ml / a little less than 1 cup).

5. Bring the tagine to the boil and then put the lid on and put in your preheated oven for 1 hour and 15 minutes.

6. Thirty minutes before the end of the cooking time, add in the chopped butternut squash and drained chickpeas. Stir everything together, put the lid back on and return to the oven for the final 30 minutes of cooking.

7. When the tagine is ready, remove it from the oven and stir through the chopped coriander. Serve with buckwheat, couscous, flatbreads or basmati rice.

Nutrition:

Calories: 401 kcal

Fat: 14g

Carbohydrates: 40g

Fiber: 8g

Sugar: 17g

Protein: 33g

67.Baked Potatoes with Spicy Chickpea Stew

Preparation Time: 10 minutes

Cooking Time: 1 hour

Servings: 6

Ingredients:

- 6 baking potatoes pricked all over
- 2 tbsp olive oil
- 2 red onions finely chopped
- 4 cloves garlic grated or crushed
- 2 cm ginger grated
- ½ tsp chilli flakes (more if you like things hot!)
- 2 tbsp cumin seeds
- 2 tbsp turmeric
- Splash of water
- 2 x 400g tins chopped tomatoes
- 2 tbsp unsweetened cocoa powder (or cacao)
- 2 x 400g tins chickpeas (or kidney beans if you prefer!), including the chickpea water DON'T DRAIN!!

- 2 yellow peppers (or whatever color you prefer!) chopped into bitesize pieces
- 2 tbsp parsley (plus extra for garnish)
- Salt and pepper to taste (optional)
- Side salad (optional)

Direction

1. Preheat the oven to 220C/200C fan/gas mark 7/425F, meanwhile you can prepare all your ingredients.
2. When the oven is hot enough put the baking potatoes in the oven and cook for 1 hour or until they are done how you like them. (Feel free to use your normal baked potato method if it's different from mine!)
3. Once the potatoes are in the oven, place the olive oil and chopped red onion in a large wide saucepan and cook gently, with the lid on for 5 minutes, until the onions are soft but not brown.
4. Remove the lid and add the garlic, ginger, cumin and chilli. Cook for a further minute on low heat, then add the turmeric and a very small splash of water and cook for another minute, taking care not to let the pan get too dry.
5. Next, add in the tomatoes, cocoa powder (or cacao), chickpeas (including the chickpea water) and yellow pepper. Bring to the boil, then simmer on low heat for 45 minutes until the sauce is thick and unctuous (but don't let it burn!). The stew should be done at roughly the same time as the potatoes.
6. Finally stir in the 2 tbsp of parsley, and some salt and pepper if you wish, and serve the stew on top of the baked potatoes, perhaps with a simple side salad.

Nutrition:

Calories: 500 kcal

Fat: 10g

Carbohydrates: 9g

Fiber: 17g

Sugar: 13g

Protein: 19g

68.Char-Grilled Steak

Preparation Time: 1 hour 40 minutes

Cooking Time: 16 minutes

Servings: 5

Ingredients:

- 1 tsp salt plus more for seasoning
- 1 tsp cornstarch
- 4 rib-eye steaks about 1 1/2" thick, around 1 pound each
- pepper

Direction:

1. In a small bowl, combine the salt and cornstarch.

2. Pat the steaks dry and rub with the salt mixture.

3. Place the steaks on a wire rack and chill in the freezer for 30 minutes to 1 hour.

4. Meanwhile, build a fire on your charcoal grill and clean the grate for when those steaks are ready to go.

5. Season the steaks with pepper.

6. Grill for 4 to 8 minutes per side (for your desired doneness – 4 is my lucky number).

7. Remove from the grill and tent with foil. Allow resting for 5 minutes before serving.

8. To serve, slice thin on an angle against the grain

Nutrition:

Calories: 472 kcal

Fat: 32g

Carbohydrates: 1g

Protein: 46g

69.Asian King Prawn Stir-Fry Together with Buckwheat Noodles

Preparation Time: 5 minutes

Cooking Time: 15 minutes

Servings: 4

Ingredients:

- 300g buckwheat/soba noodles try to get 100% buckwheat if you can
- 2 tbsp extra virgin olive oil
- 1 red onion, sliced thinly
- 2 sticks of celery, sliced
- 100g kale, roughly chopped
- 100g green beans, chopped
- 3 cm ginger, grated
- 3 cloves of garlic grated or finely chopped
- 1 bird's eye chilli seeds/membranes removed and chopped finely (or more to taste)

- 500g king prawns
- 2 tbsp tamari/soy sauce plus extra for serving
- 2 tbsp parsley chopped (or lovage if you can get it!)

Direction

1. Cook the noodles for 3-5 minutes or until they are done to your liking. Drain, rinse in cold water. Drizzle over a little olive oil, mix and set aside.
2. While the noodles are cooking, prepare the rest of the ingredients.
3. In a wok or large frying pan, fry the red onion and celery in a little olive oil over gentle heat for 3 minutes until soft, then add the kale and green beans and fry over medium-high heat for 3 minutes.
4. Turn the heat down again and add the ginger, garlic, chilli and prawns. Fry for 2-3 minutes until the prawns are hot all the way through.
5. Add the noodles, tamari/soy sauce and cook for 1 more minute until the noodles are warm again. Sprinkle with parsley and serve.

Nutrition:

Calories: 484 kcal

Fat: 10g

Carbohydrates: 65g

Fiber: 1g

Sugar: 3g

Protein: 39g

70.Fruity Curry Chicken Salad

Preparation Time: 45 minutes

Cooking Time: 0 minutes

Servings: 8

Ingredients:

- 4 skinless, boneless chicken breast halves - cooked and diced
- 1 stalk celery, diced
- 4 green onions, chopped
- 1 Golden Delicious apple - peeled, cored and diced
- 1/3 cup golden raisins
- 1/3 cup seedless green grapes, halved
- 1/2 cup chopped toasted pecans

- ⅛ tsp ground black pepper
- 1/2 tsp curry powder
- ¾ cup light mayonnaise

Directions

1. In a large bowl combine the chicken, celery, onion, apple, raisins, grapes, pecans, pepper, curry powder and mayonnaise. Mix all together. Serve!

Nutrition:

Calories: 229 kcal

Protein: 15.1g

Carbohydrates: 12.3g

Fat: 14g

Cholesterol: 44.5mg

Sodium: 188mg

Chapter 15.   **Dinner Recipes**

71.Garlicky Tomato Chicken Casserole

Preparation Time: 5 minutes

Cooking Time: 50 minutes

Servings: 4

Ingredients:

- 4 chicken breasts
- 2 tomatoes, sliced

- 1 can diced tomatoes
- 2 cloves of garlic, chopped
- 1 shallot, chopped
- 1 bay leaf
- 1 thyme sprig
- ½ cup dry white wine
- ½ cup chicken stock
- Salt and pepper to taste

Directions:

2. Combine the chicken and the remaining ingredients in a deep-dish baking pan.
3. Adjust the taste with salt and pepper and cover the pot with a lid or aluminum foil.
4. Cook in the preheated oven at 330F for 40 minutes.
5. Serve the casserole warm.

Nutrition:

Calories: 313 kcal

Fat: 8g

Protein: 47g

Carbohydrates: 6g

72.Chicken Cacciatore

Preparation Time: 5 minutes

Cooking Time: 45 minutes

Servings: 6

Ingredients:

- 2 tbsp extra virgin olive oil
- 6 chicken thighs
- 1 sweet onion, chopped
- 2 garlic cloves, minced
- 2 red bell peppers, cored and diced
- 2 carrots, diced
- 1 rosemary sprig
- 1 thyme sprig
- 4 tomatoes, peeled and diced

- ½ cup tomato juice
- ¼ cup dry white wine
- 1 cup chicken stock
- 1 bay leaf
- Salt and pepper to taste

Directions:

1. Heat the oil in a heavy saucepan.
2. Cook chicken on all sides until golden.
3. Stir in the onion and garlic and cook for 2 minutes.
4. Stir in the rest of the ingredients and season with salt and pepper.
5. Cook on low heat for 30 minutes.
6. Serve the chicken cacciatore warm and fresh.

Nutrition:

Calories: 363 kcal

Fat: 14g

Protein: 42g

Carbohydrates: 9g

73.Cauliflower Curry

Preparation Time: 5 minutes

Cooking Time: 5 hours

Servings: 4

Ingredients:

- 1 cauliflower head, florets separated
- 2 carrots, sliced
- 1 red onion, chopped
- ¾ cup coconut milk
- 2 cloves of garlic, minced
- 2 tbsp curry powder
- A pinch of salt and black pepper
- 1 tbsp red pepper flakes

- 1 tsp garam masala

Directions:

1. In your slow cooker, mix all the ingredients.
2. Cover, cook on high for 5 hours, divide into bowls and serve.

Nutrition:

Calories: 160 kcal

Fat: 11.5g

Fiber: 5.4g

Carbs: 14.7g

Protein: 3,6g

74.Herbed Roasted Chicken Breasts

Preparation Time: 5 minutes

Cooking Time: 50 minutes

Servings: 4

Ingredients

- 2 tbsp extra virgin olive oil
- 2 tbsp chopped parsley
- 2 tbsp chopped cilantro
- 1 tsp dried oregano
- 1 tsp dried basil
- 2 tbsp lemon juice
- Salt and pepper to taste
- 4 chicken breasts

Directions:

1. Combine the oil, parsley, cilantro, oregano, basil, lemon juice, salt and pepper in a bowl.
2. Spread this mixture over the chicken and rub it well into the meat.
3. Place in a deep-dish baking pan and cover with aluminum foil.
4. Cook in the preheated oven at 350F for 20 minutes then remove the foil and cook for 25 additional minutes.
5. Serve the chicken warm and fresh with your favorite side dish.

Nutrition:

Calories: 330 kcal

Fat: 15g

Protein: 40.7g

Carbohydrates: 1g

75.Seafood Paella

Preparation Time: 5 minutes

Cooking Time: 45 minutes

Servings: 8

Ingredients:

- 2 tbsp extra virgin olive oil
- 1 shallot, chopped
- 2 cloves of garlic, chopped
- 1 red bell pepper, cored and diced
- 1 carrot, diced
- 2 tomatoes, peeled and diced
- 1 cup wild rice
- 1 cup tomato juice
- 2 cups chicken stock

- 1 chicken breast, cubed
- Salt and pepper to taste
- 2 monkfish fillets, cubed
- ½ pound fresh shrimps, peeled and deveined
- ½ pound prawns
- 1 thyme sprig
- 1 rosemary sprig

Directions:

1. Heat the oil in a skillet and stir in the shallot, garlic, bell pepper, carrot and tomatoes. Cook for a few minutes until softened.
2. Stir in the rice, tomato juice, stock, chicken, salt and pepper and cook on low heat for 20 minutes.
3. Add the rest of the ingredients and cook for 10 additional minutes.
4. Serve the paella warm and fresh.

Nutrition:

Calories: 245 kcal

Fat: 8g

Protein: 27g

Carbohydrates: 20.6g

76.Full-of-veg hash recipe

Preparation Time: 10 minutes

Cooking Time: 30 minutes

Servings: 4

Ingredients:

- 750g   potatoes, peeled and diced

- 2 tbsp olive oil
- 100g   streaky bacon, roughly chopped
- 2 red onions, finely chopped
- 300g   carrots, peeled and diced
- 2 courgettes, diced
- 2 cloves of garlic, crushed
- 4 eggs
- 5g fresh flat-leaf parsley, chopped
- 1 red chilli, sliced (optional)
- ½ x 340g   jar pickled red cabbage

Direction:

1. Preheat the oven to gas 7, 220°C, fan 200°C. Bring a pan of salted water to the boil and simmer the potatoes for 5 mins, then drain and set aside.
2. Heat 1 tbsp oil in a large, ovenproof frying pan over high heat and fry the bacon for 5 mins until crisp. Add the onions, carrots, courgettes, garlic and potatoes; season and cook for 5 mins. Transfer the pan to the oven and bake for 25-30 mins until the veg is tender and golden.
3. Meanwhile, heat the remaining oil in a frying pan over medium-high heat and fry the eggs for 2-3 mins or until cooked to your liking.
4. Divide the hash between 4 plates and top each with a fried egg. Scatter with parsley and chilli, then serve with the pickled red cabbage on the side

Nutrition:

Calories: 467 kcal

Fat: 8g

Protein: 16.86g

Carbohydrates: 48.26g

77.Sweet Potato Curry Recipe

Preparation Time: 15 minutes

Cooking Time: 40 minutes

Servings: 4

Ingredients:

- 2 tbsp coconut oil
- ½ large red onion, finely diced
- 14 ounces/400g fresh tomatoes, diced (if using canned, drain the tomatoes)
- sea salt (I use about ¾ tsp & ground black pepper) to taste
- 3 cloves of garlic, minced
- 1 ½ tbsp garam masala
- 1 tsp curry powder
- ¾ tbsp paprika
- 1/4 tsp cumin
- 1 cup cooked chickpeas

- 1 lb 450g   sweet potatoes or 3 cups, peeled and cubed into 1-inch pieces
- 13.5 ounces/383g can coconut milk
- juice of 1 small lime
- 3 cups spinach

Direction:

1. In a deep pot over medium-high heat, add the coconut oil.
2. Add in the onions and tomatoes. Grind some sea salt and ground black pepper over the mixture and stir together. Lower heat to medium and allow cooking down until juices of the tomatoes are naturally released and onions are soft, for about 10 minutes.
3. Add in the chickpeas and the sweet potatoes, stirring to combine. Add in the garlic, garam masala, curry powder, paprika and cumin. Stir for about 30 seconds in the heat, until the spices become fragrant.
4. Add in the coconut milk and stir again. Bring the curry to a boil, and then reduce to medium-low so that the mixture continues to simmer for about 20 to 30 more minutes until the sweet potatoes are fully cooked through and are fork-tender.
5. Stir in the spinach and squeeze a lime lightly over the top of the curry (don't skip the lime!), stirring to combine. Remove the curry from the heat. Taste the curry and season with more salt and pepper if you desire. Allow to cool slightly and for the spinach to wilt in the heat until wilted (about 3 minutes), then serve. Enjoy!

Nutrition:

Calories: 344 kcal

Carbohydrates: 33.2g

Protein: 6.6g

Fat: 22.8g

Sodium: 452.8mg

Fiber: 6.3g

Sugar: 7.2g

78.Carrot, Courgette and Halloumi Hamburgers

Preparation Time: 20 minutes

Cooking Time: 10 minutes

Servings: 4

Ingredients:

- 1 large carrot, grated
- 1 large courgette, grated
- 225g halloumi, grated
- 2 spring onions, finely chopped
- 90g breadcrumbs
- 1 tbsp ground cumin
- 1 tbsp ground coriander
- ½ tsp salt
- 2 eggs
- 2 tbsp flour

- 4 brioche buns, halved
- 50g baby spinach leaves
- 1 large tomato, sliced
- 1 small red onion, sliced
- ½ cucumber, peeled into ribbons
- tzatziki, to serve

Direction:

1. Put the courgette in a clean tea towel and squeeze tightly to remove any liquid. Tip into a large bowl and add the carrot, halloumi, onion, breadcrumbs, cumin, coriander, salt, eggs and flour. Stir well to combine.
2. Put just over half the mixture in a food processor and pulse until the mixture starts to stick together. Return this back to the reserved mixture and mix well.
3. Divide the mixture into 4 and shape it into patties. Heat a barbecue or griddle pan to medium heat. Cook the burgers for 4-5 mins each side or until golden and cooked through.
4. Add the burger buns to the barbecue until lightly toasted. To assemble the burgers, place spinach leaves on the bottom of each bun. Top with the burger, a slice of tomato, cucumber ribbon and a spoonful of tzatziki.

Nutrition:

Calories: 659 kcal

Fat: 39.84g

Protein: 26.67g

Carbohydrates: 48.62g

79.Minted Lamb with a Couscous Salad Recipe

Preparation Time: 5 minutes

Cooking Time: 10 minutes

Servings: 2

Ingredients:

- 75g couscous
- ½ chicken stock cube made up to 125ml
- 30g   pack fresh flat-leaf parsley, chopped
- 3 mint sprigs, leaves picked and chopped
- 1 tbsp olive oil
- 200g   pack frozen BBQ minted lamb leg steaks, defrosted
- 200g   salad tomatoes, chopped
- ¼ cucumber, chopped
- 1 spring onion, chopped
- pinch of ground cumin
- ½ lemon, zested and juiced

- 50g   reduced-fat salad cheese

Direction:

1. Put the couscous in a heatproof bowl and pour over the stock. Cover and set aside for 10 mins, then fluff with a fork and stir in the herbs.
2. Meanwhile, rub a little oil over the lamb steaks and season. Cook to pack instructions, then slice.
3. Mix the tomatoes, cucumber and spring onion into the couscous with the remaining oil, cumin, and lemon zest and juice. Crumble over the salad cheese and serve with the lamb.

Nutrition:

Calories: 337 kcal

Fat: 17.38g

Protein: 31.57g

Carbohydrates: 15.14g

80. Pesto Salmon Pasta Noodles

Preparation Time: 10 minutes

Cooking Time: 20 minutes

Servings: 4

Ingredients:

- 1-pound fresh salmon
- 1 tbsp olive oil
- 1 tbsp butter

- Salt & pepper to taste
- 1/4 tsp garlic powder
- Flour for dredging
- 1/3 cup chicken broth or dry white wine
- 1/3 cup pesto (click for my recipe or use your fav jarred variety)
- 1/4 cup heavy/whipping cream
- 1/2 tsp lemon juice(optional)
- Freshly grated parmesan cheese (optional)
- 8 ounces uncooked pasta

Direction:

1. Boil a salted pot of water for your pasta and cook it al dente according to package directions.
2. Sprinkle the salmon with garlic powder and some salt & pepper. Coat it in flour on all sides.
3. In a skillet, heat the oil and butter over medium-high heat. Cook the salmon for about 3 minutes/side until lightly golden.
4. Take the pan off the heat. Remove the salmon to a plate and set it aside. Pour the fat out of the skillet, but leave the nice browned bits that are stuck on the bottom of the pan (don't wipe the pan out).
5. Add the chicken broth and pesto and return the pan to the burner. Cook for about 30 seconds while scraping up the brown bits from the bottom of the pan.
6. Add in the cream and lemon juice and let the sauce bubble for about a minute. Add the salmon back in and break it into pieces with your spoon. Reduce the heat and let it gently cook for another 5 minutes or so (the sauce will thicken up as well).
7. Drain the pasta and toss it with the sauce. Serve immediately with freshly grated parmesan cheese if desired.

Nutrition:

Calories: 462 kcal

Fat: 30.37g

Protein: 29.01g

Carbohydrates: 18.23g

81.Chicken liver along with tomato ragu

Preparation Time: 5 minutes

Cooking Time: 40 minutes

Servings: 4

Ingredients:

- 2 tbsp olive oil
- 1 onion, finely chopped
- 2 carrots, scrubbed and diced
- 4 cloves of garlic, finely chopped

- ¼ x 30g pack fresh basil, stalks finely chopped, leaves torn
- 380g pack chicken livers, finely chopped, any sinew removed and discarded
- 1 400g -tin Grower's Harvest chopped tomatoes
- 1 chicken stock cube, made up to 300ml
- ½ tsp caster sugar
- 300g penne
- ¼ Suntrail Farms lemon, juiced

Direction:

1. Heat 1 tbsp oil in a large nonstick saucepan, over low-medium heat. Fry the onion and carrots for 10 mins, stirring occasionally. Stir in the garlic and basil stalks and cook for 2 mins more. Transfer to a bowl; set aside.

2. Return the pan to high heat and add the remaining oil. Add the chicken livers and stir-fry for 5 mins until browned. Return the onion mixture to the pan and stir in the tomatoes, stock and sugar. Season, bring to the boil, then simmer for 20 mins until reduced and thickened, and the liver is cooked through. Meanwhile, cook the pasta to pack instructions.

3. Taste the ragu and add another pinch of sugar or more seasoning, if needed. Add a squeeze of lemon juice to taste and stir in half the torn basil leaves. Divide the pasta between 4 bowls, spoon over the ragu and top with the remaining basil.

Nutrition:

Calories: 325 kcal

Fat: 14.93g

Protein: 22.39g

Carbohydrates: 32.63g

82.Rita's 'rowdy' enchiladas

Preparation Time: 15 minutes

Cooking Time: 55 minutes

Servings: 4

Ingredients:

- 2 large chicken breasts (about 400g)
- 2 red peppers, thinly sliced
- 1 tbsp olive oil
- ¾ tsp mild chilli powder
- 1½ tsp ground cumin
- ¾ tsp smoked paprika

- 80g grated mozzarella
- 8 plain tortilla wraps
- 65g mature Cheddar, grated
- 10g fresh coriander, roughly chopped

For the sauce

- 1 tbsp olive oil
- ½ onion, finely chopped
- 2 cloves of garlic, crushed
- 500g tomato passata
- ½ tsp dried oregano
- 1 tbsp chipotle chilli paste
- 400g tin black beans, drained and rinsed
- ½ lime, juiced

Direction:

1. Preheat the oven to gas 5, 190°C, fan 170°C. Put the chicken in a 20 x 30cm baking dish with peppers, oil, chilli powder, cumin and paprika. Mix to coat, then cover with foil. Roast for 25-30 mins until the chicken is cooked through and tender and no pink meat remains. Remove the chicken from the dish and shred using 2 forks. Set aside in a large bowl.
2. Meanwhile, make the sauce. Heat the oil in a saucepan over low heat and cook the onion and garlic for 10 mins. Stir in the passata, oregano and chipotle chilli paste; increase the heat to medium, bring to a simmer and cook for a further 10 mins, stirring occasionally. Add the beans and lime juice; season.
3. Mix one-third of the sauce and half the mozzarella into the shredded chicken and peppers.
4. To assemble, spoon 4 tbsp of the sauce into the same baking dish as before. Spoon a little of the chicken mixture down the center of each tortilla, roll up and put in the baking dish. Repeat with all the tortillas and filling, placing them side by side so they don't unravel. Pour the remaining sauce over the top, then scatter over the Cheddar and remaining mozzarella. Bake in the oven for 20-25 mins until the cheese has melted and started to brown. Scatter with the coriander to serve.

Nutrition:

Calories: 582 kcal

Fat: 26.83g

Protein: 51.92g

Carbohydrates: 34.35g

Chapter 16.   **Lean and Green**

83. Sizzling Chicken Fajita Salad

Preparation Time: 15 minutes

Cooking Time: 45 minutes

Serving: 4

Ingredients:

SALAD DRESSING & MARINADE:

- 1 c. oil and vinegar dressing
- 1/4 tsp. McCormick Grill Mates Mesquite Spice Rub
- 2 tsp. jalapeño hot sauce
- 4 boneless

PICO DE GALLO:

- 1 lb. plum tomatoes
- 1 small onion
- 1/4 c. choppped cilantro
- 2 tbsp. fresh lime juice
- 1 tsp. chopped garlic
- 1/4 tsp. salt

GRILLED ONION:

- 1 large sweet onion

SALAD:

- 1 bag cut-up hearts of romaine lettuce, or 8 cups torn romaine

Directions:

1. Make Salad Dressing & Marinade: Whisk ingredients in a bowl until blended. Reserve 1/3 cup to dress the salad. Put chicken breasts and 1/2 cup Marinade in a large ziptop bag. Refrigerate about 45 minutes.
2. Combine Pico de Gallo ingredients in a bowl. Cover; leave at room temperature.
3. Grill Onions: Heat outdoor grill or a large stovetop grill pan.
4. Brush the onion slices with remaining Dressing.
5. Remove chicken from marinade; discard bag with marinade. Grill chicken and onion 5 minutes on each side, or until chicken is cooked through and onion is tender. Transfer chicken and onion to a cutting board.
6. Toss lettuce with reserved Salad Dressing. Divide among 4 serving plates. Cut chicken in strips, onion slices in half. Serve on salad along with Pico de Gallo and accompaniments.

Nutrition:

Calories: 172 kcal

Fat: 7.9g

Carbs: 6.7g

Sugar: 3.1g

Protein: 18.1g

Cholesterol: 52 mg

84.Triumph of Cucumbers and Avocados

Preparation Time: 20 minutes

Cooking Time: 15 minutes

Serving: 4

Ingredients:

- 12 oz cherry tomatoes, cut in half
- 5 small cucumbers, chopped
- 3 small avocados, chopped
- 1/2 tsp ground black pepper
- 2 tbsp olive oil
- 2 tbsp fresh lemon juice
- 1/4 cup fresh cilantro, chopped
- 1 tsp sea salt

Directions:

1. Add cherry tomatoes, cucumbers, avocados, and cilantro into the large mixing bowl and mix well.
2. Mix together olive oil, lemon juice, black pepper, and salt and pour over salad.
3. Toss well and serve immediately.

Nutrition:

Calories: 442 kcal

Fat: 37.1g

Carbs: 30.3g

Sugar: 9.4g

Protein: 6.2g

Cholesterol: 0mg

85.Crab and Asparagus Frittata

Preparation Time: 20 minutes

Cooking Time: 10-12 minutes

Serving: 6

Ingredients:

- 8 eggs
- 1/3 cup milk
- ¼ cup grated Parmesan cheese
- 1 tbsp snipped fresh tarragon or basil
- ½ tsp black pepper
- ¼ tsp salt
- 2 tsp olive oil
- ¼ cup chopped onion
- 3 cloves of garlic, minced
- 1 1/2 cups bias-cut fresh asparagus (1-inch pieces)
- 2 tbsp water
- 6 ounces fresh or canned lump crab meat, drained, flaked, and cartilage removed
- 1/3 cup bottled roasted red sweet peppers, drained and chopped
- 2 tbsp snipped fresh Italian parsley
- bottled hot sauce (optional)

Direction:

1. Preheat broiler. In a bowl whisk together the first six ingredients (through salt).
2. Heat oil in a large broiler-proof skillet over medium heat; add the onion and garlic. Cook 2 minutes. Add asparagus and the water. Cover and cook for 4 to 5 minutes or until asparagus is tender. Drain and discard any liquid remaining in the skillet.
3. Evenly sprinkle the crab and roasted peppers over asparagus. Pour egg mixture over vegetables and crab in skillet. Cook over medium heat. As mixture sets, run a spatula around edge of skillet, lifting egg mixture so uncooked portion flows underneath. Continue cooking and lifting edges until egg mixture is almost set (surface will be moist).
4. Place skillet under the broiler 4 to 5 inches from heat. Broil 1 to 2 minutes or until the top is just set. (Or preheat oven to 400°F; bake about 5 minutes or until the top is set.)

5. Cut into wedges. Sprinkle with parsley and serve with hot sauce.

Nutrition:

Calories: 231

Fat: 16.17g

Carbs: 6.5g

Sugar: 9.4g

Protein: 14.72g

Cholesterol: 830mg

86.Broccoli Cheese Breakfast Casserole

Preparation Time: 20 minutes

Cooking Time: 25 minutes

Serving: 6

Ingredients:

- 12 eggs, beaten with a fork
- 2 tbsp cream, half and half, or milk
- 1 tsp. Spike Seasoning (Or use any all-purpose seasoning that's good with eggs.)
- fresh ground black pepper to taste

- 3 cups broccoli florets
- 1/4 cup grated Swiss cheese
- 1/4 cup grated Mozzarella cheese
- 1/4 cup grated sharp cheddar cheese (see notes)

Direction:

1. Preheat oven or toaster oven to 375 degrees. Spray a glass casserole dish with nonstick spray. (I use a 7.25 X 11.25 inch pan for this size, but it can be a little larger if you don't have that size.)
2. Cut broccoli into flowerets about 1 inch across.
3. Put broccoli into a pot with enough water to cover and bring to a boil. As soon as the water boils and broccoli turns bright green (less than 5 minutes). Immediately, drain broccoli into a colander.
4. While broccoli cools, break eggs into a mixing bowl. Add milk or half and half, Spike Seasoning (affiliate link), and black pepper and beat eggs until ingredients are well combined.
5. Put the well-drained broccoli into a casserole dish. Sprinkle cheeses over broccoli.
6. Pour eggs over broccoli-cheese, then use a fork to gently stir so that broccoli and cheeses are evenly distributed throughout the eggs.
7. Bake at 375 degrees for about 25 minutes, or until the top is slightly browned and eggs puff up slightly.
8. Serve hot, with sour cream if desired.
9. This will keep in the fridge for several days and can be reheated in the microwave or in a hot frying pan.

Nutrition:

Calories: 242 kcal

Total Fat: 15g

Saturated Fat: 6g

Unsaturated Fat: 7g

Cholesterol: 389mg

87.Bibimbap Bowls

Preparation Time: 15 minutes

Cooking Time: 20 minutes

Serving: 4

Ingredients:

Rice

- 4 cups cooked jasmine rice

Sauteed Spinach

- 1/2 tbsp cooking oil
- 6 cups fresh spinach, loosely packed
- 1 tsp toasted sesame oil

- Pinch of salt

Chili Garlic Beef

- 1/2 lb ground beef
- 2 tbsp chili garlic sauce
- 1 tbsp soy sauce
- 1 tbsp brown sugar

Fresh Vegetables

- 1 carrot
- 1 cucumber
- 2 green onions

Other Toppers

- 4 large eggs
- 1/4 cup kimchi
- 1 Tbsp sesame seeds

Instructions

1. If your rice is not already cooked, begin that first and prepare the rest of the bowl ingredients as the rice cooks. You'll need 4 cups of cooked rice.
2. Prepare the sautéed spinach next. Heat a large skillet over medium flame and add the cooking oil. Swirl to coat the skillet, then add the fresh spinach. Sauté the spinach for a few minutes, or just until it is wilted. Drizzle the sesame oil over top and season lightly with a pinch of salt. Remove the spinach from the skillet to a clean bowl.
3. Add the ground beef to the skillet used to cook the spinach. Cook the beef until fully browned, then add the chili garlic sauce, soy sauce and brown sugar. Stir and cook for about one minute, or until everything is evenly mixed and the beef is coated in sauce. Turn the heat off.
4. Prepare fresh vegetables. Peel and grate the carrot using a large-holed cheese grater. Thinly slice the cucumber, and slice the green onions.
5. Fry or soft boil 4 large eggs (Or however many bowls you plan on eating immediately. If meal prepping, cook the egg fresh each day.)
6. Build the bowls by first adding 1 cup cooked rice to the bowl, followed by 1/4 of the cooked spinach, 1/4 of the ground beef, some sliced cucumber, shredded carrots, a cooked egg, a tbsp or so of kimchi.

Sprinkle sliced green onions and sesame seeds over top. There are no hard measurements needed for each ingredient per bowl, just divide the ingredients evenly, or as you see fit.

Nutrition:

Calories: 327.55 kcal

Carbohydrates: 20.83g

Protein: 12.58g

Fat: 11.45g

Sodium: 1003.28mg

Fiber: 3.13g

88.Mini Bacon Cheeseburger Bites

Preparation Time: 15 minutes

Cooking Time: 25 minutes

Serving: 27

Ingredients:

- 27 crispy crown potatoes (found in the freezer section)
- 3/4 lb lean ground beef
- 2 pinches salt
- 2 pinches fresh ground pepper
- 2 pinches onion powder

- 3 slices yellow American cheese
- 3 slices crispy cooked bacon

Direction:

1. Preheat oven to 400 degrees.
2. Arrange crispy crowns in a single layer on baking sheet. Bake 20 minutes turning halfway through.
3. Meanwhile in a small bowl mix ground beef, salt, pepper and onion powder. Shape into little patties about 1 inch round and relatively flat. Place in a single layer on separate baking sheet. Place in oven and bake 10 minutes flipping halfway through.
4. Divide each cheese and bacon slice into ninths. On baking sheet top each crispy crown with a burger, cheese slice and bacon. Place back in the oven until the cheese is melted; approximately 2-3 minutes.

Nutrition:

Calories: 124.55 kcal

Carbohydrates: 8.1g

Protein: 11.6g

Fat: 4.9g

Sodium: 693g

89.Mongolian Beef

Preparation Time: 10 minutes

Cooking Time: 25 minutes

Serving: 4

Ingredients:

- 1-pound flank steak
- 1/4 cup cornstarch
- 1/4 cup canola oil
- 2 tsp fresh ginger, minced
- 1 tbsp garlic, minced
- 1/3 cup lite soy sauce, low sodium
- 1/3 cup water
- 1/2 cup dark brown sugar

Direction:

1. 4 stalks scallions, green parts only, cut into 2-inch pieces
2. Slice the flank steak against the grain (the grain is the length of the steak) the long way 1/4 inch think pieces and add it to a Ziploc bag with the cornstarch.
3. Press the steak around in the bag, making sure each piece is fully coated with cornstarch and leave it to sit.
4. Add the canola oil to a large frying pan and heat on medium-high heat.
5. Add the steak, shaking off any excess cornstarch, to the pan in a single layer and cook on each side for 1 minute.
6. If you need to cook the steak in batches because your pan isn't big enough do that rather than crowding the pan you want to get a good sear on the steak and if you crowd the pan your steak with steam instead of sear.
7. When the steak is done, remove it from the pan.
8. Add the ginger and garlic to the pan and sauté for 10-15 seconds.
9. Add the soy sauce, water and dark brown sugar to the pan and let it come to a boil.
10. Add the steak back in and let the sauce thicken for 20-30 seconds.
11. The cornstarch we used on the steak should thicken the sauce, if you find it isn't thickening enough add 1 tablespoon of cornstarch to 1 tablespoon of cold water and stir to dissolve the cornstarch and add it to the pan.
12. Add the green onions, stir to combine everything, and cook for a final 20-30 seconds.
13. Serve immediately.

Nutrition:

Calories: 433 kcal

Calories: 433g

Carbohydrates: 37g

Protein: 27g

Fat: 20g

Saturated Fat: 3g

Cholesterol: 68mg,

90.Taco Mason Jar Salad

Preparation Time: 25 minutes

Cooking Time: 15 minutes

Serving: 4

Ingredients

- 1 Tbsp. Olive oil
- ¾ cup red onion, finely diced
- 1 lb. lean ground beef 93/7

Taco Seasoning Mix:

- 1 ½ Tbsp. cumin
- 1 ½ tsp. paprika
- 1 tsp. chili powder

- ¾ tsp. salt
- ½ tsp. pepper
- ⅛ tsp. cayenne pepper

Mason Jar Taco Salads:

- ¼ cup salsa medium
- ¼ cup ranch dressing
- 1 cup whole kernel corn, rinsed and drained
- 1 cup black beans, rinsed and drained
- 1 cup tomatoes, finely diced
- ½ cup cheddar cheese shredded
- 1 large avocado, cut into ½-inch cubes
- 4 cups mixed greens
- 20 corn tortilla chips crushed
- Find your Whole Foods Market 365

Direction:

1. In a large skillet over medium heat add olive oil and chopped red onion. Sauté for 3-4 minutes or until almost cooked through.
2. Push onions to the side and add lean ground beef. Sauté for 7-8 minutes or until cooked through.
3. While beef is cooking mix together cumin, paprika, chili powder, salt, pepper and cayenne pepper in a small bowl.
4. Once ground beef is done cooking, turn off the heat and add seasoning ingredients. Mix to combine. Using a potato masher or the back of your fork, crumble the ground beef to your desired consistency.
5. In a small bowl whisk together the salsa and ranch.
6. In four 24-oz. wide mouth mason jars add equal amounts of the salsa-ranch, ground beef mixture, corn, beans, tomatoes, and cheese. Store in the refrigerator for up to 5 days.
7. The morning before serving, add ¼ of the avocado, 1 cup of greens, and crushed corn tortilla chips.
8. Shake the Mason jar well before pouring contents into a large salad bowl to enjoy.

Nutrition:

Calories: 531 kcal

Carbohydrates: 35g

Protein: 35g

Fat: 29

91.Easy Salmon Florentine

Preparation Time: 10 minutes

Cooking Time: 20 minutes

Serving: 4

Ingredients

- 4-5 Salmon Fillets skin on
- 2 tbsp Olive Oil divided
- 3 large cloves of garlic pressed
- 5 oz Fresh Spinach, roughly chopped, about ¾ Cup
- 6 oz Button Mushrooms sliced, ¾ cup
- ¼ cup Vegetable Broth

- ¾ cup Coconut Cream
- Kosher salt and pepper, to taste

Direction

1. Rinse the fish and pat dry with a paper towel, then place it into the prepared baking tray.
2. Season with some salt and pepper. Heat 1 Tbsp of oil in a large non-stick pan over medium heat. Add salmon, skin side up, and cook undisturbed for 4-5 minutes, until golden.
3. Gently flip the fillets on the other side, and continue to cook for 4-6 minutes, or until cooked through and skin is crispy.
4. Once the salmon is done, set aside on a plate. Heat remaining oil in the same pan over medium-high heat. Add garlic and cook until fragrant.
5. Add mushrooms and cook until slightly golden brown and tender. Add broth and coconut cream, season with salt and pepper, if needed.
6. Reduce the heat to low and let it simmer until sauce is thickened, then stir in spinach and cook until wilted, 1-2 minutes.
7. Return the salmon back to the pan, and spoon the creamy spinach and mushrooms on top. Serve hot and enjoy!

Nutrition:

Calories: 565 kcal

Carbohydrates: 42g

Protein: 36g

Fat: 27g

Saturated Fat: 11g

Cholesterol: 94mg

Sodium: 192mg

92.Shrimp and Creamy Cauliflower Grits

Preparation Time: 30 minutes

Cooking Time: 30 minutes

Serving: 4

Ingredients

- 1 large head cauliflower (about 2 pounds), trimmed and cut into small florets
- 1 cup 1 percent-milk
- 3 tbsp unsalted butter
- Kosher salt and freshly ground black pepper
- 1/3 cup grated Parmesan
- 1 1/4 pounds peeled and deveined tail-on medium shrimp
- 2 large cloves of garlic, minced
- Pinch cayenne pepper, optional
- 2 tbsp roughly chopped fresh parsley

- Juice of 1/2 lemon, plus lemon wedges, for serving

Direction:

1. Pulse about half of the cauliflower in a food processor until the florets break down into finer pieces about the size of grains of rice (it's totally fine if they clump; think of this step as cauliflower "rice" gone wrong). Transfer to a medium saucepan, pulse the remaining cauliflower and add that to the pan too. Add the milk, 1 tablespoon of the butter, 1/2 tsp salt and several grinds of pepper and bring to a simmer over medium-high heat. Simmer, stirring frequently, until the mixture is soft and smooth and looks like grits about 10 minutes. Remove from the heat, stir in the Parmesan and adjust the seasoning with more salt and pepper if you'd like. Cover and keep warm.

2. Season the shrimp with salt and pepper. Melt the remaining 2 tablespoons butter in a large skillet over medium-high heat. Add the shrimp, garlic and cayenne if using and cook, tossing, until the shrimp are pink and just cooked through 3 to 4 minutes. Remove from the heat, add the parsley, lemon juice and 1 tablespoon water and stir to coat the shrimp with the sauce. Season with salt and pepper.

3. Divide the cauliflower grits among shallow bowls and top with the shrimp and sauce. Serve with lemon wedges.

Nutrition:

Calories: 152 kcal

Carbohydrates: 12.94g

Protein: 7.19g

Fat: 8.56g

Conclusion

Ever feel that you could use some help in losing weight and feeling better!

Well, what if I told you that there is a way to lose weight and much more by simply following the Optavia Diet system. The Optavia diet is a 5-Phase system (like a step-by-step table of contents for you) that is truly amazing. It will help you to lose weight and to feel great about it. Every step is based on the principle of a low-calorie diet product a key ingredient in the plan to help you feel great while you lose weight. Each phase is designed to transition into a healthier way of eating that gradually will help you lose weight in the fastest way possible.

It is based on both the latest science and the principle of moderation. It is no secret that many successful people have become successful because of their remarkable ability to master the delicate balance between making important choices and controlling their lives. For example, they are extremely strict with routine and discipline, and they follow a certain lifestyle that will certainly give them the advantage of being successful.

But at the same time, they are not so strict that they will be about to crash from poor lifestyle choices, and they will not have a poor time in life. It is quite common for people to make bad decisions and have poor time in life. For example, consuming more than their bodies can handle and having poor health that will affect them in the future.

It's just a matter of everyone making good choices and following a healthy lifestyle that will make a difference in their lives. Optavia diet is that kind of choice. It is a choice that would allow you to be able to become successful by being able to achieve your weight-loss goals fast.

In other words, it is a great way for you to make a positive change in your life simply. Not only is the new system that you are using so easy to follow, but it will give you the edge that many people need in their life, for example, by simply having the ability to have a good night's rest.

Wake up, feeling rested and ready to start the day. This is what it will allow you to do. As you read further, you will understand why it is in your best interest to consider getting this Optavia diet product seriously. It gives you everything that you need to accomplish a lot in life.

In the end, people often spend their lives stubbornly refusing to accept the sacrifices they are forced to make to achieve their goals. Optavia's diet is no different. It is a product you need to take action now and truly look into it. It offers its users something that many people would consider as almost a guarantee to master and achieve their goals in life.

It proves this by providing those people with a weight-loss product that works! For example, it allows people to achieve the weight loss they are after, by having the superior systems that it uses to help. There are many things that this product offers users that few others can.

This product is also quite affordable and can work for many different people. It has been proven to work for people of all age groups and of all different types. If you are the type of person that likes to avoid making changes, then you can comfortably continue to do so.

But if you are the type of person who is looking for a greater level of change in your life, then you must try getting this Optavia diet product. It will give you much more than you could have ever imagined.

In the end, the true measure of a person is not always determined by whether they are able to achieve their goals or not. It is only when a person is able to achieve their goals, but they are also able to make other people feel happy and successful with them. This is a sign that they will be able to integrate both their professional and personal lives with a much greater accomplishment.

CPSIA information can be obtained
at www.ICGtesting.com
Printed in the USA
LVHW070958250221
679534LV00016B/11